Men and Women of Science

The World Book Encyclopedia of Science

Volume
8

Men and Women of Science

•

Index

World Book, Inc.

a Scott Fetzer company

Chicago

Acknowledgments

Publisher William H. Nault

Editorial
Editor in chief—Robert O. Zeleny
Executive editor—Dominic J. Miccolis
Associate editor—Anne M. O'Malley
Senior editor—Katie John Clark
Contributing editor—Robert N. Knight
Permissions editor—Janet T. Peterson
Writer/editor—Waldemar Bojczuk

Art
Art director—Roberta Dimmer
Assistant art director—Joe Gound
Photographs director—John S. Marshall
Product coordinator—Kelly M. Shea

Product production
Executive director—Peter Mollman
Director, manufacturing—Henry Koval
Manager, manufacturing—Sandra Van den Broucke
Director, pre-press services—Jerry Stack
Product managers—Madelyn Krzak—Christina Shirven
Proofreaders—Anne Dillon—Marguerite Hoye
              Esther Johns—Daniel J. Marotta

Contents

Men and Women of Science

Hippocrates

Hippocrates (460?-377? B.C.), a physician of ancient Greece, is known as the father of modern medicine. His principles of medical science formed the basis for modern medical theory developed in the 1800's. His famous oath, the Hippocratic oath, is still used today. Usually, graduating medical students take an oath modeled after the oath of Hippocrates. It defines the relationship of doctor to patient and affirms a doctor's duty to humanity.

Hippocrates established medical theory on rational, scientific principles. He believed that diseases had only natural causes, not supernatural ones. Furthermore, Hippocrates regarded the human body as a whole organism. He treated patients in what we would call a holistic manner—with proper diet, fresh air, and attention to habits and living conditions.

Some of the medical techniques Hippocrates used were quite advanced for his time. For instance, he performed surgery, such as boring holes into the skull to relieve pressure from a tumor. He also used tar as a crude antiseptic for wounds.

Hippocrates was born on Kos, a Greek island. Little is actually known about his life. More than 70 treatises on medicine and scientific research have come down to us from Hippocrates. In ancient times, these were gathered in a famous collection and kept at the great library of Alexandria, Egypt. Some of the works were almost certainly written by others, perhaps pupils of Hippocrates. But the number actually written by Hippocrates himself is unknown.

Hippocrates as pictured in a 19th century steel engraving

Aristotle

Aristotle (384-322 B.C.) was one of the greatest thinkers of the ancient world. Aristotle was deeply interested in the philosophy of nature, devoting much thought to the relationship between form and matter and the nature of change. Another important area of thought for Aristotle was the nature of knowledge itself. Aristotle's ideas strongly influenced the development of thought in Western civilization, especially through the Middle Ages in the Christian nations of Europe and the Islamic world.

In addition to his philosophic contemplations, Aristotle collected a large number of observations about the physical world, particularly of living things. In fact, Aristotle may be considered the first great biologist. He examined the structure of plants and animals and observed the behavior of animals. He also classified living things in groups according to their common traits rather than their usefulness to humans.

One measure of Aristotle's influence on the modern world is the large number of words in modern languages that can be traced back to his teaching and writings. For example, the terms of grammar, *subject* and *predicate,* come from Aristotle. Also, many words used to describe basic scientific principles are Aristotle's. These include *matter, energy, potential, cause, genus, species,* and many others. Mathematics relies on such vocabulary as *quantity, relation*—also words of Aristotle. Many of these words have come into modern languages through Latin, rather than directly from Greek.

Aristotle was born the son of a physician who attended the king of Macedonia. At the age of about 18, he entered the great philosopher Plato's school in Athens, the Academy. Aristotle remained at the Academy

Ancient Times to A.D. 1450

Hippocrates establishes the fundamental principles of medical science.

 ca. 400 B.C.

Democritus proposes the first known atomic theory of matter.

 ca. 345 B.C.

Aristotle develops theories about the nature of matter; he provides proofs of the earth's spherical shape.

for about 20 years, then joined a group of Plato's disciples for some 3 years afterward. In about 343 B.C., Aristotle went to the court of King Philip II of Macedonia to supervise the education of Alexander, the king's son. Aristotle thus had the opportunity to influence the future world conqueror, Alexander the Great. After Alexander reached maturity, Aristotle returned to Athens and founded the Lyceum, his own school. The method and philosophy associated with the Lyceum came to be known as *peripatetic*—a Greek word for walking about—because Aristotle taught while walking with his students. In 323 Aristotle fled the Athenians, who had trumped up a charge against him, and settled in the city of Chalcis, where he spent his final year.

Relatively few of Aristotle's written works survive. We know of the existence of many more because of references in the works of other writers of ancient times.

Archimedes

Archimedes (287?-212 B.C.), a great mathematician, physicist, and inventor of the ancient Greek world, made profound contributions to several mathematical and scientific fields. Unfortunately, much of his theoretical work was lost—although some, such as the *Method Concerning Mechanical Theorems,* have been recovered in modern times. In the latter work, Archimedes attempted to describe the technique he used to arrive at useful mathematical values, such as the relationship between the volume and surface area of a sphere. He had hoped that other scholars would use his method to make further discoveries. Most of Archimedes' writings show the careful methodology he used to formulate scientific and mathematical theories.

Archimedes also made fundamental discoveries in hydrostatics, a branch of physics that deals with fluids. Archimedes formulated a principle of buoyancy, or apparent loss in weight experienced by a body when placed in a liquid. His principle asserts that an object placed in liquid seems to lose an amount of weight that is equal to the weight of the fluid it has displaced. The famous story of Archimedes running out of his bath and into the street shouting "Eureka" relates his excitement at rec-

Aristotle *(right)* with Plato *(left)* as pictured by Raphael

ognizing this principle.

Archimedes also refined the value of *pi,* which is used to calculate certain dimensions of circles and spheres. He used numbers in ways that prefigured the modern science of calculus.

In his day, Archimedes was widely known and popular for his inventions. These include the Archimedean screw, a type of pump, and the catapult, used by warriors to throw stones at opposing troops.

Archimedes lived most of his life in Syracuse, a Greek city on the island of Sicily. He is

Archimedes establishes fundamental principles of experimental science.

ca. 240 B.C.

Aristarchus proposes a theory that the earth revolves around the sun.

Hipparchus discovers the precession of the equinoxes; he develops a system of star classification by magnitude.

ca. 135 B.C.

7 B.C.

Strabo, a Greek geographer and historian, completes the 17-volume *Geography,* which noted that the rising and sinking of lands was due, partially, to volcanoes and earthquakes.

believed to have studied at Alexandria, the great classical center of learning in Egypt. Archimedes was killed by a Roman soldier in 212 B.C., possibly against orders, when the Romans invaded and captured Syracuse. Of his many writings, nine treatises in Greek exist today. We know that many have been lost because of numerous references to such works in other writings that survive from ancient times.

Galen

Galen (A.D. 130?-200?), an important physician of ancient Rome, is often called the father of experimental physiology. Physiology is the study of the structure of living things. Galen earned this name because he dissected (cut apart) many animals and drew medical conclusions that applied to human beings. During the Middle Ages, Galen was considered one of the foremost medical authorities.

Galen realized that the Barbary ape, a monkey from Africa, was similar in some ways to human beings. Since the Roman laws of his time prevented Galen from dissecting humans, he reasoned that he could learn much about the human body by dissecting monkeys. He made many accurate observations, especially about the heart and circulatory system. For instance, Galen found that arteries carry blood. Up to that time, physicians had thought that the arteries carry air to body parts. Galen described the valves of the heart and the differences between veins and arteries. He also made important observations about bones, muscles, and nerves.

Some of Galen's theories **have been** disproved by modern medical science. For instance, Galen thought that four main substances called *humours*—phlegm, black bile, yellow bile, and blood—must be in balance in the body for a human to be healthy. This idea was regarded as medical fact for many centuries.

Galen was born in Pergamum in Asia Minor (now Bergama, Turkey). He studied medicine and philosophy in several centers of Greek learning, including Alexandria, in Egypt. He returned to Pergamum, where he was appointed

Galen as pictured in a 19th century French engraving

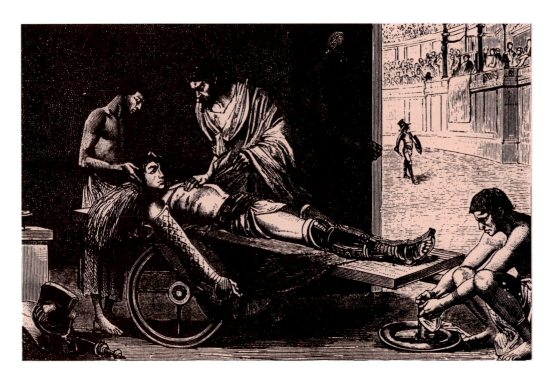

Pliny the Elder, a Roman scholar, writes the 37-volume *Historia Naturalis* that recorded all Roman knowledge of rocks, minerals, and fossils. Pliny died in A.D. 79 observing the eruption of Vesuvius that destroyed the city of Pompeii.

Rhazes, a Persian-born physician, describes measles and smallpox.

ca. A.D. 70   ca. A.D. 150   ca. A.D. 175   ca. A.D. 900   ca. A.D. 1000

Ptolemy formulates the classical system of astronomy, which was accepted in the West for nearly 1,500 years.

Galen discovers certain principles of the circulation of blood in animals and humans.

Avicenna, an Arab physician, produces a medical encyclopedia that accurately describes meningitis, tetanus, and many other diseases.

a physician to the gladiators. Gladiators were fighters who fought other gladiators or wild animals in public arenas to entertain the public.

Galen's fame spread, and he went to Rome. There he became a physician to the emperors. Little is known about the final years of Galen's life.

Roger Bacon

Roger Bacon (1214?-1292?) was an English philosopher and scientist, a major early supporter of experimental science. Bacon was known widely and popularly in his day and gained the title *doctor mirabilis,* which is Latin for "wonderful teacher." Bacon conducted studies in many fields, including mathematics, astronomy, optics, and alchemy, an early form of chemistry. Though he described spectacles and gave exact directions for making gunpowder, Bacon is most remembered today for his insistence on using the experimental method to confirm scientific theories. His scientific skepticism and commitment to method and experimentation were well known in his own day. Bacon's own most significant researches, those in the field of optics, reveal careful experimentation and interpretation of results.

Roger Bacon was born into a wealthy English family and enjoyed the educational advantages his social rank afforded. He was educated at Oxford University and later at the University of Paris, where he also taught. Around 1247, Bacon returned to Oxford, where he seems to have undergone a considerable change in his thinking, possibly due to the influence of the great scholar Robert Grosseteste. Thus began for Bacon an intensive, decade-long period of scientific research. The year 1257 marked another great change in Bacon's life, for the scientist-scholar joined the Franciscan religious order. From this time until his death in or around 1292, Bacon's career was enmeshed in politics of the pope and the Franciscan order. He was even imprisoned for a time by the Franciscans for controversial writings. Nevertheless, Bacon managed to produce a large volume of writings in the period from 1257 until his death.

In his greatest treatise, the *Opus Maius*

(Longer Work), Bacon urged the pope to undertake a program of educational reform in which new areas of scientific study would be opened in universities of the West. The death of the somewhat sympathetic Pope Clement IV in 1268 ended Bacon's hopes for these plans.

Nicolaus Copernicus

Nicolaus Copernicus (1473-1543), a Polish astronomer, developed the theory that the earth is a planet that revolves around the sun. This idea, which came to be known as the Copernican theory, changed the way we look at the earth's place in the universe. For this reason, the Copernican theory is considered one of the most important scientific advances in history. Also, Copernicus is considered the founder of modern astronomy.

Since the time of ancient Rome, astronomers had accepted a system of the universe developed by Ptolemy, who had lived in the A.D. 100's. Even in the time of Copernicus, some 1,300 years later, Ptolemy's ideas were accepted as fact. The Ptolemaic system, as Ptolemy's scheme was called, was regarded with respect and even awe. The authorities of church and state supported this and other ideas that had held sway for many centuries.

Ptolemy had developed a very complicated model of the universe to explain the variety of astronomical observations made before and during his time. His model placed the earth at the center of the universe. On earth was change, but the rest of the universe beyond was changeless. Some movements of bodies in the skies puzzled Ptolemy. For instance, the planets seemed to vary in brightness and to move backwards at times. But Ptolemy devised a series of circles on which he supposed the planets moved. This solution seemed to satisfy the problems posed by the planets' movements.

Copernicus, an experienced astronomer and Renaissance thinker, became dissatisfied with the Ptolemaic system. Ptolemy's solutions to such contradictions as planetary movements seemed forced. Also, Copernicus had read the writings of a number of ancient Greeks. Some had suggested that the sun, not the earth, was the center point around which the planets revolved.

The Renaissance——1450-1600

Roger Bacon establishes certain principles of the modern, empirical scientific method.

ca. 1247

ca. 1514

Nicolaus Copernicus formulates the theory that the earth revolves around the sun; this overthrows the 1,500-year-old Ptolemaic system.

Nicolaus Copernicus as pictured in a 17th century Flemish engraving

NICOLAVS COPERNICVS

Gradually, Copernicus accepted the sun-centered solar system. He spent a long time working out his ideas. Around 1514 he circulated among his friends a written report that set forth his new theories. His report, entitled "A Commentary on the Theories of the Motions of Heavenly Objects," put forward several related ideas about the earth and the heavens. Some of the ideas were as follows: (1) that the earth rotates daily on its axis; (2) that the earth revolves around the sun once each year; (3) that the sun is the center of the system of the planets, including the earth; and (4) that the earth is the center only of the moon's orbit.

Copernicus was apparently afraid to publish his theories for a long time. He realized how revolutionary they were and what angry opposition they might arouse. Although Pope Clement VII heard Copernicus' theories and approved them in 1533 in Rome, Copernicus continued to delay. Finally, friends and pupils persuaded Copernicus to let them publish his theories. A pupil named Georg Rhäticus took the manuscript to Germany. But in the German city of Nuremberg, he ran into the opposition of the reformers Martin Luther and Philipp

Melanchthon. Rhäticus then went to Leipzig, another German city, and turned the manuscript over to Andreas Osiander. It is Osiander who finally published the work, *On the Revolutions of the Heavenly Spheres,* in 1543, the last year of Copernicus' life.

Copernicus planned *On the Revolutions of the Heavenly Spheres* as a mathematical system that would replace the Ptolemaic system. The work included six main sections. In the first section, Copernicus asserted that the earth, like the other planets, moves around the sun. He also set out the order of the planets around the stationary (nonmoving) sun. Copernicus' order was the one we now know to be correct: the sun, Mercury, Venus, Earth, Mars, Jupiter, and Saturn. (The outer planets—Uranus, Neptune, Pluto—had not been discovered when Copernicus was living.)

In the third section, Copernicus concentrated on the Earth's motion. In the remaining sections, he considered the movements of the moon and the other planets.

Copernicus was pleased with his astronomical system, because it accounted for the observed movements in the skies more easily than the Ptolemaic system. As other scientists realized how well the Copernican theory matched the observed facts, more and more of them accepted it. In his lifetime, Copernicus was not able to prove his theories. But other scientists after him, especially Galileo and Kepler, would do so.

The ideas of Copernicus started new ways of thinking. For this reason, their effect on civilization is often described as "the Copernican Revolution." According to Copernicus, the earth was not the center of the universe, but only one of several planets. Also, the universe described by Copernicus seemed much larger than before. It was a vast arena of change, rather than changeless and fixed. These ideas affected the way people thought of themselves in relation to the greater universe. Moreover, scientific ideas about gravity had been based on belief in an earth-centered universe. These ideas now had to be reworked. In the 1600's, Sir Isaac Newton would propose new theories on gravity and create a new system of physics.

 ca. 1540

 1543

Andreas Vesalius publishes a treatise containing the first accurate anatomical portrayal of the human body.

Philippus Aureolus Paracelsus pioneers the application of chemistry to medicine.

Nicolaus Copernicus was born into a well-to-do family in eastern Poland. He was given the Polish name *Mikolaj Kopernik.* For professional purposes, he used the Latinized form of the name, Nicolaus Copernicus. This was a common practice throughout Europe at the time. As a young man, Nicolaus gained a position as a canon, a salaried church official, at the cathedral in Frauenburg (now Frombork, Poland). Nicolaus was fortunate enough to have as his uncle a bishop, who obtained the position for him. It gave him economic security for his lifetime.

The young Copernicus studied at several of Europe's finest universities. These included the universities at Kraków in Poland, and Bologna, Padua, and Ferrara, in Italy. He gained a thorough Renaissance education, including mathematics, astronomy, medicine, and theology. He also learned Greek and Latin and became familiar with classical writings in these languages. Despite the profound effect of his theories on the world, Copernicus lived a rather quiet life. He died at Frauenburg on May 24, 1543.

Andreas Vesalius

Andreas Vesalius (1514-1564) is known as the father of anatomy. (Anatomy is the scientific study of body structures in humans and other animals.) He made and published the first complete, accurate descriptions of the human anatomy. His important contributions paved the way for future advances in medical science.

For over a thousand years, doctors and medical scientists had accepted the writings of Galen, a physician of ancient Rome, as absolute. Galen had left records of his dissection methods—that is, the methods he used to cut open organisms for study. Vesalius was the first modern anatomist to question Galen's authority. He realized that Galen had dissected only animals such as pigs or monkeys—not human beings.

Vesalius developed his own procedures for dissecting a cadaver (a dead human body). He performed numerous dissections and made careful records on everything he saw. In time, Vesalius had gathered enough data to publish.

His great work on anatomy, *On the Fabric of the Human Body*—often called *Fabrica,* from its Latin name—appeared in 1543. *Fabrica* presented the most complete and accurate picture of human anatomy up to that time. Furthermore, the book demonstrated some of the potential of the printing press. It contained a number of beautiful and elaborate anatomical drawings made from carved wood blocks. These detailed illustrations helped spread Vesalius' observations quite rapidly.

Though very controversial, *Fabrica* made a great impact on medical science. Vesalius identified and described body structures that had not been known before. Anatomists wondered what functions these structures served. They conducted further investigations, which eventually led to new advances in medical science.

Vesalius was born in 1514 to a family of distinguished physicians and pharmacists (people who prepare drugs for medical uses). He received a thorough education, studying at universities in Louvain (modern Belgium), Paris, and Padua, Italy.

In 1543, the year of publication of *Fabrica,* Vesalius was appointed personal physician to the Holy Roman Emperor, Charles V. Vesalius later received a lifelong pension from Charles and gained appointment as personal physician to the emperor's son, King Phillip II of Spain.

In 1564 Vesalius and his wife went on a pilgrimage to the Holy Land. On the trip back, Vesalius became ill and was put ashore on a Greek island. He apparently died there, though the exact date of death is not known.

Vesalius drawing, originally published in 1543, showing the structure of the human muscle system

Tycho Brahe

Tycho Brahe (1546-1601) was a Danish astronomer of the Renaissance. Brahe developed a careful, systematic approach to observation of the heavens and accurately fixed the positions of hundreds of stars. Brahe's accomplishments are all the more remarkable in that he did all his work without aid of the telescope.

In 1572, Brahe discovered a supernova, an exploding star then visible from earth for the first time. Brahe's discovery, published the next year, shook the European scientific community almost as rudely as had the Copernican

---

Georgius Agricola, a physician from Saxony, writes *De Re Metallica,* which becomes the basis for modern studies and books on metallurgy and mining.

| ca. 1550 | 1556 | 1572 |

Ambroise Paré introduces surgical techniques that anticipate modern surgery, earning him the title "father of modern surgery."

Tycho Brahe sights a supernova, or exploding star, which disproves the ancient idea that the heavens cannot change.

theory a generation before. (In 1543, Copernicus had published the theory that the earth and all the planets revolve around the sun. This new Copernican theory rejected the ancient system of astronomy known as the Ptolemaic system.) An important concept of the Ptolemaic astronomical system was the assumption that change never occurs in the heavens. Brahe's startling discovery uprooted this foundation of traditional astronomy. Brahe never himself accepted the Copernican theory. His work, however, enabled his pupil and assistant, Johannes Kepler, to confirm the Copernican theory.

A true Renaissance figure, Brahe traveled and studied widely in central Europe. For a time in the 1570's and 1580's, Brahe enjoyed the lavish patronage of Denmark's King Frederick II. This Renaissance monarch granted Brahe an island (Ven) near Copenhagen on which to build an astronomical observatory. With financial support from the king, Brahe constructed his observatory and laboratory, which he named Uraniborg. During its heyday, Uraniborg became something of a scientific

mecca, receiving learned persons from all over Europe. In true Renaissance spirit, Brahe and his royal patron attracted artists and craftspersons from far and wide to design and decorate the facilities at Uraniborg. With the accession of King Christian IV in 1588, however, Brahe's relationship with king and state began to sour. Brahe finally left Denmark in 1597, then settled in Prague, where he obtained the support of the Holy Roman Emperor Rudolf II for the final years of his life.

Galileo

Galileo Galilei (1564-1642) was an Italian scientist and mathematician who made profound contributions to the scientific revolution that was occurring before, during, and after his lifetime. Galileo's work advanced knowledge in astronomy and physics. His methods for approaching and solving a scientific problem helped shape the experimental method in science. In fact, Galileo is often called the founder of modern experimental science. He is also called the founder of the science of mechanics, the study of motion.

Galileo's foremost interest was astronomy. He made many important contributions in this field. Galileo happened to live in a time when one invention was following fast upon another. Around the year 1600 a crude telescope had been invented. Galileo greatly improved the telescope and began to observe the skies with it in 1609. He rapidly made a number of discoveries in astronomy. He was the first person, for instance, to see that the moon's surface is rough and irregular. He discovered the moons of Jupiter and the rings of Saturn. Galileo also discovered sunspots and found that the planet Venus goes through phases similar to our moon.

Galileo's spectacular findings thoroughly convinced him of the truth of the Copernican theory about the solar system. This theory, which had first been published by Nicolaus Copernicus in 1543, proposed that the earth and all the other planets revolve around the sun, which is at the center of our solar system. Though this idea seems unremarkable to modern minds, it was at first regarded as extremely radical. For about 1,400 years, astronomers had accepted the model of the universe that

Drawing of a celestial sphere from **Tycho Brahe's** *Astronomiae instauratae Mechanica,* published in 1602

The Seventeenth Century——1600-1699

 ca. 1600

William Gilbert provides a foundation for the study of electricity and magnetism.

Galileo as pictured in *Before the Inquisition,* an 1847 painting, by Robert-Fleury

Ptolemy, an ancient Roman astronomer, had developed. That model, called the Ptolemaic system, put the earth at the center of the entire universe. It held that the sun and all the other planets revolve around the earth. An elaborate system of thought had developed around the Ptolemaic system. It touched on physics, philosophy, and other areas of thought and study. Clearly, a rejection of the Ptolemaic system would bring about a revolution in scientific thought and in other areas of thought as well.

In Galileo's time, the Copernican theory was still highly controversial. In the Roman Catholic Church, many officials connected the new scientific thinking with the spread of Protestant ideas. These fears made many church officials generally suspicious of new ideas. All of these factors led Galileo into trouble. The fame he enjoyed as teacher, lecturer, and scientific experimenter only made matters worse.

In 1616 the Roman Catholic Church decreed that church members—which included nearly everyone in Catholic countries—could not think of the Copernican theory as an idea that might be proved true. They could discuss the theory only by treating it as completely hypothetical, that is, imaginary. Galileo received a personal warning on this issue.

Galileo made every reasonable attempt to comply with church restrictions. On the other hand, he continued to write and think about astronomy. In 1632, Galileo published a book comparing the Ptolemaic and Copernican systems. The book, which championed the Copernican theory, became a great popular success in Europe. In the meantime, the Inquisition reopened Galileo's case. The Inquisition was an institution of the Roman Catholic Church that

Galileo improves the telescope and observes the heavens; he helps found modern scientific method.

ca. 1610

sought out and tried heretics, people who defy church teaching. In 1633 Galileo was called to Rome to stand trial before the Inquisition. On pain of execution, Galileo was forced to recant, that is, publicly reject, his views about the Copernican theory. He was sentenced to house arrest, which lasted for the remainder of his life. Despite this turn of events, the Copernican theory gained complete acceptance within a generation or two. And about 350 years later, in 1979, Pope John Paul II declared that the church may have been mistaken in condemning Galileo.

Galileo made fundamental contributions to the physics of motion, called mechanics. In this work, he laid a foundation for the revolutionary mathematical principles introduced by Sir Isaac Newton a few years later. Galileo developed a new theory of motion consistent with a moving earth. This work grew out of Galileo's acceptance of the Copernican theory, for in the older, Ptolemaic system, the earth was believed to be motionless. A number of related ideas emerged. One was the law of the pendulum—that pendulums of equal length swing at the same rate whether their arcs are large or small. Another was the law of falling bodies, which states that all objects fall at the same speed, regardless of their mass. Galileo's important book, *Discourse on Two New Sciences,* which appeared in 1638, described some of his experimental work in this area and the conclusions he had drawn. Late in life, Galileo suggested how his discoveries about pendulums could be used in clocks. A Dutch scientist, Christiaan Huygens, eventually put these suggestions into practice.

Galileo, born Galileo Galilei, received an early education in a monastery and was later sent to the University of Pisa to study medicine. The young man's interest, however, shifted to mathematics, and he soon managed to study science and mathematics.

Galileo first made his mark with the invention of the hydrostatic balance. The function of this device was to find the specific gravity of objects by weighing them in water. Teaching positions in mathematics followed, first in Pisa, then in Padua. In later life, Galileo devoted most of his efforts to experimentation and writing. His problems with church authorities made teaching and lecturing impractical.

Galileo became blind in the last few years of his life. Despite this hardship, he continued to work on scientific problems and to correspond with other scientists until his death in 1642.

Johannes Kepler

Johannes Kepler (1571-1630) was a great German scientist and mathematician who contributed to a modern understanding of the planets' motion around the sun. Kepler also founded the modern science of optics (the study of light and vision) and expanded the geometric system founded by the ancient Greeks.

As a young student, Kepler was introduced to the theories of Nicolaus Copernicus by his astronomy teacher, Michael Mästlin. Copernicus had published, in 1543, the theory that the earth and the planets revolve around the sun. This was a revolutionary idea, because astronomers had accepted for almost 1,500 years the belief that the earth is the center of the universe. Even in Kepler's youth, some years after Copernicus' publication, the Copernican theory generated a great deal of controversy.

Spurred by thoughts of Copernicus and his own training, Kepler began to think about the motions of planets. He still held to the notion that the planets (and all other heavenly bodies) moved in perfect circles. This too was an idea that had come from the ancient Greeks. They saw the universe beyond the earth's atmosphere as changeless and perfect. To the Greeks, perfection was symbolized by the circle. So they believed that all celestial bodies (stars and planets) moved in paths that were circular or combinations of circles.

Kepler applied the ancient Greeks' idea, but with a modification. He tried to fit planetary motion into complex series of "perfect" geometric figures. He regarded the figures as perfect, because they were all made up of equal sides and had been identified by the ancient Greeks as perfect. The attempt did not work; Kepler had to find another solution to the riddle of planetary motion.

Eventually, Kepler realized that the planets travel around the sun in an elliptical (oval-shaped) path. This knowledge upset many previous beliefs about the solar system and uni-

Johannes Kepler formulates the laws of planetary motion.

ca. 1618

verse. Most importantly, it demolished the age-old belief in universal circular motion. Kepler went further. He formulated three new laws of planetary motion. The first law states the basic idea that all the planets travel in elliptical orbits around the sun. The second law states that a planet always sweeps out the same area in its orbit in an equal period of time. The logical conclusion of this law is that a planet moves faster when it is closer to the sun. The third law states a mathematical formula relating the planets' mean distance from the sun to the time it takes them to complete an orbit.

Moreover, Kepler made public some observations he had made of a supernova in 1604-1605. A supernova is an exploding star. The supernova could be seen in the skies for over a year. This event further eroded the ancient belief that the distant heavens remain changeless. Clearly, a very dramatic change in a distant star had been observed.

Kepler published a book in 1618 that strongly supported the theories of Copernicus. He was the first astronomer to support Copernicus openly. (Only a few years later, Galileo would be put to trial by the Roman Catholic Church for supporting the Copernican theory.)

Johannes Kepler made fundamental contributions to our understanding of optics—the way in which we see. He is sometimes called the father of modern optics. Kepler explained how the human eye works. First, scattered light enters the eye. Ideally, the light is focused by the pupil to a single point on the retina, which is light-sensitive. (Sometimes the light comes to a focal point either in front of or behind the retina. This is the cause of blurred vision.)

Kepler also extended the understanding of

Johannes Kepler *(left)* with Emperor Rudolf II at Prague as shown in a 19th century German engraving

geometry that had been passed down from the ancient Greeks. He described new three-dimensional forms and devised formulas to determine their volume. Kepler's inspiration for this work came from his dealings with wine merchants. No standard to measure volume existed in the wine industry of Kepler's time. Using whatever vessels they had, wine merchants roughly estimated the volume of wine they sold to customers. Kepler believed he was being cheated.

Johannes Kepler was born in southwestern Germany in 1571. Although from a poor family, he was granted a scholarship by the Duke of Württemberg, the local ruler, to study at the University of Tübingen. (Tübingen is a city in southwestern Germany.) Johannes had originally intended to become a Lutheran pastor, but he became a mathematics teacher instead. He obtained a teaching position in a school at Graz, Austria. While teaching, young Kepler found time to write on astronomy.

Kepler's work came to the attention of Tycho Brahe, who invited him to join his staff at an observatory near Prague. (At that time a part of a central European empire, Prague is today the capital of Czechoslovakia.) Brahe, the foremost astronomer in Europe, was supported by the Holy Roman Emperor, whose capital was then at Prague. Brahe died in 1601, and Kepler succeeded him as astronomer and mathematician to the emperor.

Although a follower of the new science and learning, Kepler had a painful personal experience of the continuing superstition of his time. In 1620 his mother was accused of witchcraft and made to stand trial. (A few years later, the Puritans in Massachusetts also conducted witchcraft trials.) Conviction would carry the sentence of being burned at the stake. Kepler staked his reputation on his mother's innocence, and she was acquitted.

Johannes Kepler died in 1630 at Regensburg, Germany.

Francis Bacon

Francis Bacon (1561-1626) was an English statesman and philosopher whose name is associated with the development of modern experimental science. Bacon, a contemporary of Shakespeare, lived in the exciting, intellectually rich times of Queen Elizabeth I and King James I in England. He displayed the intellectual curiosity and active way of life that typified Renaissance individuals.

Bacon believed that human reason, if armed with the proper logical methods, could gain command over nature and in so doing, greatly improve the human condition. In his greatest philosophical work, *Novum Organum,* Bacon developed a system of reasoning to gain such knowledge of the natural world.

Bacon felt that certain "idols," or causes of logical error in human reasoning, stand in the way of learning and that these must be removed before true knowledge can be attained. He identified four such idols. The first idol, according to Bacon's analysis, is the tendency of human reasoning to perceive more simplicity and unity than actually exist. This category also includes the fault of drawing a conclusion from an isolated event that seems more significant than it really is. An example of this idol would be predicting future calamities on the basis of a total eclipse of the sun.

A second idol is identified as intellectual prejudices that are unique to an individual. This is the intellectual fault of judging matters on the basis of one's own education, experience, and taste, and using such judgments as a basis for "knowledge." Bacon felt that such factors are wholly unreliable in the pursuit of knowledge.

A third idol is the lack of precision in human communication, that is, in language. Bacon noticed that distinctions made by words are often very inexact. For example, the word *fish* was often used in his day for both *fish* and *whale*—although these animals are very different.

Bacon's fourth idol is previously held philosophies and laws of logic. From Bacon's perspective this was a particularly powerful idol, because throughout the Middle Ages systems of thought developed by ancient philosophers were regarded as faultless. But Bacon himself lived in a time when such ideas and philosophies were being questioned and overturned on every side.

Having removed these stumbling blocks to sound reasoning, a person could then use inductive reasoning to gain true knowledge, according to Bacon. Inductive reasoning is the process by which we make observations about particular things or events and then proceed to a more general statement of principle—when enough such observations have been

1620

Francis Bacon publishes *The New Atlantis,* which describes a modern research institution. This and earlier works by Bacon contribute to the modern scientific method.

Another important and innovative aspect of Bacon's thought is his vision of science as a collaborative effort in which individuals use methods of reasoning such as Bacon had described and contribute collectively to the good of humankind. In his utopian work, *The New Atlantis,* Bacon described a research institution equipped with tools of modern science such as laboratories, printing presses, and libraries. In time, this vision proved to be remarkably prophetic.

Francis Bacon was born in London to a well-to-do family. His father had risen from relatively modest origins to become a high government official. Bacon was also connected through family ties to other persons of high rank, notably Robert Cecil, chief minister of the crown under both Elizabeth I and James I. Bacon studied at Cambridge University, then went to France for a time as a member of the English ambassador's court. As a young man, Bacon pursued a legal career and was elected to Parliament in 1584. Ambitious and active at court, Bacon attempted to gain position through Robert Devereux, the Earl of Essex, a favorite of Queen Elizabeth. Later, in 1601, Bacon served as the Queen's counsel in the trial of Essex for treason. After James I came to the throne in 1603, Bacon worked carefully to gain favor with the king. In 1603, he was made a knight. By 1618 he had obtained appointment as lord chancellor and several years later was created Viscount St. Albans, a title of nobility. But in 1621 Bacon, having fallen out of favor with James I, was convicted of taking bribes, fined, and imprisoned for a time. He never regained his former status at court. Bacon died in 1626.

Francis Bacon's chief philosophical writings were *The Advancement of Learning* (1605) and *Novum Organum* (1620). Both of these works were intended to be part of a six-volume work called *Instauratio Magna* that Bacon never completed.

Effigy of **Francis Bacon** in St. Michael's Church, St. Albans, England

verified. Bacon made several crucial points about inductive reasoning. One is that the experimenter must make careful and methodical observations and must collect a great deal of observed data before making a general conclusion based on that data. Another point is that negative experimental findings carry greater weight than positive ones. The reason for this is that a single negative finding can disprove a theory, but many positive results are required to prove it.

William Harvey

William Harvey (1578-1657) was an English physician who discovered how blood circulates in the human body. Harvey's discovery ranks as one of the greatest in medical history. Without this knowledge, medical doctors

 1628

William Harvey publishes a landmark treatise on the human heart and the circulation of blood.

could not have understood the most basic functioning of heart, lungs, arteries, and veins. Harvey's scientific methods also helped establish basic standards for biological research.

The ancient Greeks, including Aristotle, believed that blood vessels contain both blood and air. They also thought that blood moves through the body rather like the tides in the seas, slowly ebbing and flowing. According to these theories, the force behind blood circulation was rhythmic contractions in the blood vessels. The heart was believed to have no role in this activity. These ideas about the circulatory system held their ground into the 1600's.

One physician of ancient times, Galen, who lived in the A.D. 100's, rejected the idea that blood vessels contain air. He thought, correctly, that they contain only blood. But Galen learned nothing new about circulation of the blood.

In the 1500's, some anatomists (medical scientists who study anatomy) began to learn more about the heart, lungs, and blood circulation. One of the great Italian anatomists of this time was Andreas Vesalius. Vesalius and others formed theories about the pulmonary circulation in the body. The word *pulmonary* refers to the lungs, and pulmonary circulation describes the circular movement of blood between the heart and lungs. Also, an Italian anatomist named Fabricius discovered the system of valves in the veins. Despite these findings, the process by which blood circulates remained unknown to medical doctors and scientists.

It was William Harvey who learned the true nature of blood circulation and made this knowledge public. In 1628 Harvey published the book, *An Anatomical Treatise on the Motion of the Heart and Blood in Animals*. He explained that the heart works as a pump, forcing the blood to move outward in the arteries to all parts of the body. The heart's pumping continues without pause until death. Thus, a continuous stream of blood is always moving through the blood vessels. Harvey also explained the function of veins—that they return blood back to the heart. The valves in veins help move blood in the direction of the heart.

Harvey also explained pulmonary circulation. And he rejected once and for all the belief that blood vessels contain air.

Harvey's book made him famous and caused a great controversy. His ideas about blood circulation were so new and radical that many people could not accept them. Some people attacked him viciously in their writings. Harvey ignored the attacks. Finally, in 1649, he published a book in answer to the criticisms of a French anatomist, Jean Riolan. Harvey used this opportunity to demolish many of the objections people had made to his theory. Harvey lived to see wide and general acceptance of his ideas.

Harvey made another great contribution to medical science in his study of animal reproduction. In 1651 he published his experimental findings and theories in a book called *Anatomical Excitations Concerning the Generation of Living Creatures*. Harvey studied chick embryos to learn how living things reproduce. He concluded that an embryo begins in the egg and gradually develops into a fully formed organism. This idea of the embryo's gradual formation is known as *epigenesis*. Posed against epigenesis was a theory called *preformation*, the belief that the embryo is fully formed from the beginning, although tiny. Harvey's observations and theories laid the foundation for the modern science of embryology.

Harvey's great scientific insights came from his careful observations and scientific methods. Harvey dissected every specimen he could obtain. He also attended or performed post-mortem examinations whenever possible. A post-mortem is the dissection of a human body after death. Such examinations are often conducted to determine the cause of death, especially if any doubt or suspicion exists.

William Harvey was born in Folkestone, a town in the far south of England, in 1578. The Harveys were a prosperous family, and William and his brothers enjoyed wealth throughout their lives. William began his schooling at a cathedral school of Canterbury Cathedral, a great English cathedral. Harvey later attended Cambridge University, earning a degree in 1597. He then studied medicine at the University of Padua, in Italy. At that time—around 1600—the medical school at Padua had the greatest reputation of any in Europe. Harvey's schooling there gave him the opportunity to study under the great Italian anatomist, Fabricius.

Harvey returned to England in 1602 and began practicing medicine. Around the year 1618, Harvey was appointed physician to King James I. This was the beginning of a long, and politically turbulent, association with the Stu-

René Descartes introduces the modern philosophy of rationalism, which contributes to the human will for knowledge and to the modern scientific method.

 ca. 1637-1644

art kings. (Stuart was the family name of a line of English kings and queens.) The son of James I succeeded him as Charles I in 1625. Harvey remained as personal physician to the king.

The reign of Charles I saw increasing conflict between the king and the Puritans, who controlled Parliament. In the 1640's this conflict broke into open civil war, leading to the execution of the king in 1649. William Harvey was closely associated with the king, to whom he remained loyal. As a result, Harvey got into deep political trouble. He was banned from practicing medicine in London's chief hospitals. Also, soldiers of the Puritans in Parliament destroyed his scientific papers. Only Harvey's private lecture notes survived. For several years he was kept under house arrest in the home of one of his brothers.

Throughout his career, Harvey enjoyed the respect and good will of his professional peers. In 1652 he donated his personal library to the College of Physicians in London. Tragically, the library was destroyed in the Great Fire of London only 14 years later (1666).

William Harvey died in 1657 and was buried in the family vault. Over 200 years later, in 1883, his body was moved to the Harvey Chapel, a memorial to him.

René Descartes

René Descartes (1596-1650) founded a school of philosophy, called *rationalism,* which provided the foundation for modern science—specifically scientific method. Descartes lived at a time when science was on the verge of tremendous advances. His philosophy helped create a climate in which scientists could develop new ideas and test their ideas according to scientific and mathematical principles. For this reason, Descartes has been called the father of modern philosophy. Descartes also made important specific contributions to mathematics and science.

As a young man, Descartes was concerned with the question, "how do I know what is real, that is, what exists?" After great mental struggle, Descartes believed he had arrived at the basis of all knowing. He summed up this realization in the famous statement, "I think, therefore I am." Descartes felt he might doubt the true existence of everything around him—but the very fact that he could think and doubt proved the existence of his own mind. This system of philosophy, which starts with the mind as the basis of all reality, is called *rationalism.*

From this starting point, Descartes developed a thorough method for gaining and testing knowledge. He wrote about his method in several books. In *Discourse on Method,* published in 1637, Descartes presented his basic philosophy and examined certain scientific questions. He endorsed William Harvey's ex-

Portrait of **René Descartes**
by Frans Hals

1651

William Harvey publishes a treatise that establishes the foundation of the science of embryology.

planation of blood circulation in the human body, for example. Descartes wrote the *Discourse* in his native French language, rather than Latin, then the language used for scholarly works. He may have wanted educated people outside of universities to read and discuss his ideas.

In a book called *Rules for the Direction of the Mind* (or *Regulae* in Latin), Descartes presented his method in even greater detail. He defined a set of rules for attaining truth. His first rule urged "never [to] accept anything as true which I [do] not clearly and distinctly see to be so." Descartes never published *Regulae.* It was printed about 50 years after his death.

An important aspect of Descartes's basis of thought was the idea that all knowledge is uniform. In this idea, Descartes broke sharply with the philosophy of the Middle Ages, known as scholasticism. The philosophers of scholasticism had claimed that different kinds of knowledge are distinct, just as "knowable objects" are distinct. But Descartes insisted that the power of knowing, that is, of the mind, is always the same.

Descartes also insisted that all properties of the physical world could be described in quantitative, that is, mathematical terms. This means that physical laws of the universe act upon all objects—whether rocks or living organisms—in the same ways.

The rationalistic philosophy developed by Descartes proved extremely important to the development of science. It encouraged scientific (and other) thinkers to question all previous "knowledge" until tested and confirmed. It also helped scientists to view the universe in strictly physical, mathematical terms. Within a few years of Descartes's death, Sir Isaac Newton developed an entirely new system of physics. From the middle 1600's to our present day, scientific knowledge has expanded at an ever-increasing pace. Descartes probably deserves some credit for these developments. At the very least, his ideas and writings helped break down resistance to the new ways of thinking.

Descartes made specific contributions to mathematics and science. He developed the modern branch of mathematics known as analytic geometry. He formulated the law of refraction and gave a scientific explanation for rainbows. Descartes dissected many animals and made observations on anatomy.

René Descartes was born into a well-to-do family in La Haye, France, in 1596. (The village

"The Nature of Vision," a woodcut from **Descartes's** *Tractatus de Homine,* published in 1686

of his birth is now called La Haye-Descartes.) René's father was a lawyer, and the young Descartes was expected to follow in this profession. Even as a small child, however, René earned the name "the little philosopher" from his father. Apparently, the little boy asked constant questions about the causes and reasons for things.

Descartes did complete his law education, but he decided not to pursue a career in the legal profession. This decision caused tension between René and his father. Nevertheless, the young Descartes inherited property from his mother, which provided him with a living and allowed him freedom.

Descartes tried the military life for a time. He served in armies of several princes—allies of the French king—who were engaged in the Thirty Years' War (1618-1648). Later, Descartes lived in Paris and enjoyed its busy social life. Yet even during these youthful years, Descartes was observing "the book of the world" and contemplating problems of philosophy.

In 1628 Descartes settled in Holland, where he would spend most of his remaining years. During these 20 years, Descartes devoted himself to thinking, writing, and investigating scientific and mathematical problems. Descartes published several books in which he presented and explained his philosophy. These include *Discourse on Method* (1637), *Meditations on First Philosophy* (1641), and *Principles of Philosophy* (1644).

Like other creative thinkers of his time, Descartes stirred up controversy and got into trouble with authorities of church and state. He had planned to publish a comprehensive philosophical work, *The World,* in 1633. In this book, Descartes strongly endorsed the Copernican theory, which stated that the earth and the planets revolve around the sun. Then Descartes heard from a friendly church official that Galileo had just been condemned in Rome. Galileo's crime had been to publish a book in support of the Copernican theory. Descartes decided to withdraw his own book. It did not appear in print until after his death.

Later, Descartes got into trouble with Dutch authorities for the ideas he had expressed in the book, *Meditations on First Philosophy.* (The book had been published in 1641 and translated into French in 1647.) Eventually, the Roman Catholic Church put Descartes's books on the *Index,* a list of books Catholics were forbidden to read.

William Boyle and Robert Hooke build air pumps with which they investigate vacuums.

ca. 1655   1660

The Royal Society, an organization to promote the natural sciences, is founded in London.

Queen Christina of Sweden, 23 years of age and a great admirer of Descartes, urged the French philosopher to come to her court at Stockholm. Although he regarded Sweden as the "land of bears between rock and ice," Descartes reluctantly decided to go there in 1649. In February, 1650, Descartes caught pneumonia and died. Although buried in Sweden, Descartes's remains were returned to France for reburial in 1667. Eventually, the French people considered Descartes a great national hero.

Robert Boyle

Robert Boyle (1627-1691), an Anglo-Irish scientist, was a founder of modern chemistry and founding member of the Royal Society of London. Boyle conducted fundamental experiments on gases. He also attacked anciently held scientific theories, including Aristotle's notion that the universe is made up of the four elements: earth, air, fire, and water. Instead, Boyle proposed that all matter is composed of primary particles (which he called "corpuscles") that combine in different ways and proportions to produce different substances. Boyle's "corpuscular" theory laid the groundwork for development of a modern atomic theory in the nineteenth century.

Boyle demonstrated through experiments that air is necessary for fire, breathing, and sound. Experimentation led him to conclude a basic property of gases, which came to be known as Boyle's law: the volume of a gas at a constant temperature varies inversely to the pressure applied to the gas. Boyle also proposed a method to distinguish acids from alkalines.

Although born in Ireland, Boyle was a Protestant and lived mostly in England as an adult. He displayed considerable interest in religion, especially in later life, and wrote a theological work, *The Christian Virtuoso,* in 1690. Boyle also published numerous works on his experiments, including a treatise on gases in 1660 and a work presenting his theory of matter in 1661.

Marcello Malpighi

Marcello Malpighi (1628-1694) was the first anatomist to use the microscope extensively. An anatomist studies the structures of plant and animal bodies. Malpighi's discoveries changed the course of several sciences that are concerned with structures of living organisms. His work also had a major impact on the practice of medicine.

When Malpighi was a young man, the microscope was a very new invention. The first modern compound microscope had been invented shortly before the year 1600. A compound microscope uses two lenses to magnify images, while a magnifying glass uses only one. The compound microscope opened to scientists new worlds that had never been seen before.

Throughout his scientific career, Malpighi continually observed and described the microscopic world. Over a lifetime, he amassed a large volume of scientific information.

In 1661 Malpighi described capillaries he had viewed with the aid of the microscope. Capillaries are tiny blood vessels that connect veins and arteries. Malpighi's discovery gave support to William Harvey's theory of blood circulation. Harvey had published his theory in 1628 that the heart pumps blood outward through the arteries to all parts of the body. He also said that the blood returns to the heart through veins. But Harvey could not explain how the blood gets from the arteries to the veins. Malpighi's capillaries provided the answer.

Malpighi was also the first person to see red blood cells in the blood. He also reasoned (correctly) that the red color of blood is due to the many, many red blood cells carried by the blood fluid.

Malpighi identified many other tiny structures in the body through use of the microscope. He studied tissues in the brain, the kidney, spleen, liver, and bone. He examined and described the optic nerve—the nerve that connects the eye to the brain. He also identified and described taste buds. Malpighi identified a deep layer of the epidermis (skin), which is now named for him.

In all of these discoveries about human body tissue, Malpighi made very important contributions to histology and to practical medicine. (Histology is the study of body tissues at the microscopic level.)

An engraving of **Robert Boyle's** first air pump, published originally in Boyle's *The Spring and Weight of the Air,* 1660

Robert Boyle publishes a book that describes his theory of matter.

 1661

Marcello Malpighi describes capillaries viewed through a microscope.

Malpighi's scientific interests went beyond human anatomy. He studied many insect larvae. (A larva is an insect form at a particular stage of its development.) One of the insects he studied and described was the silkworm. This is a particularly valuable insect to humans, because it produces silk fibers that can be woven into cloth.

Another area of science that benefited from Malpighi's discoveries is embryology, the study of newly developing organisms, such as chicks in eggs. Malpighi identified several microscopic structures of the chick embryo (fertilized baby chick inside the egg).

Additionally, Malpighi conducted an extensive survey of microscopic plant structures. He compared these plant structures and his work laid much of the groundwork for the modern science of botany (the study of plants).

Marcello Malpighi was born in 1628 in a small town near Bologna, Italy. He received an excellent education, first from his father at home, then at the University of Bologna. Malpighi received a doctoral degree in medicine in 1653.

Malpighi taught in several prominent Italian universities, including those in Pisa, Bologna, and Messina (on the island of Sicily). His observations and discoveries became generally known—and controversial. Malpighi's work attracted the attention of the Royal Society of London (formed in 1660). The Society encouraged Malpighi to inform them of his discoveries by writing letters. Many of the letters were published in the Royal Society's journal, *Philosophical Transactions.* The Royal Society made Malpighi an honorary member in 1669. He was the first Italian to be offered membership in the society.

Meanwhile, Malpighi's published discoveries were causing strife in Italy. Today we accept many of Malpighi's observations as scientific fact. But in the 1600's, many people clung to ideas about the physical and biological world that had been held for centuries. Such ideas often had almost the authority of religious doctrine.

In 1684 a mob in Bologna turned violent and burned Malpighi's home. They destroyed his scientific papers and his microscopes. Malpighi's career was in ruins. Eventually, the pope invited Malpighi to come to Rome and serve as his personal physician (doctor). This appointment removed Malpighi from the violent controversy surrounding him and gave him the pope's protection for the few years that remained to him. Malpighi died in 1694.

Anton van Leeuwenhoek

Anton van Leeuwenhoek (1632-1723) was an amateur Dutch scientist who made a large number of observations of microscopic life and structures of organisms. Leeuwenhoek also produced ample writings and illustrations to record and publish his observations. The first human to see microbes (microscopic organisms), Leeuwenhoek is sometimes considered the father of microbiology.

Leeuwenhoek hand-ground his own lenses and made his own microscopes. His exact method of viewing objects under the microscope, however, is unknown. Leeuwenhoek's lenses could magnify objects up to about 270 times their size. But some of the objects he saw and described were much smaller than that.

Around 1674, Leeuwenhoek began to observe tiny living organisms under the microscope. He called these *animacules,* meaning "tiny animals." Based on his descriptions, we now know that Leeuwenhoek's animacules included bacteria and protozoa, both one-celled organisms. In 1683 the Royal Society of London published the first known drawing of bacteria, which had been submitted by Leeuwenhoek.

Leeuwenhoek was also the first person to observe spermatozoa, the reproductive cells produced by the male sex of many animals. This was an especially important discovery, because before this time no one knew exactly how the egg is fertilized to start a new organism (for example, a human baby).

Leeuwenhoek observed and described parts of human and other animal bodies. Most importantly, he described the red blood cells in detail in 1684. (Marcello Malpighi had discovered these cells about 18 years earlier but had not given a detailed description of them.) Leeuwenhoek also described parts of the eye and striations (stripes across the fibers) in certain kinds of muscle tissue.

A major part of Leeuwenhoek's work was the study of small insects and their developmental stages. He was one of the first modern

Robert Hooke observes and describes cells in cork.

1665   **ca. 1665-1666**

Isaac Newton conducts his first investigations on gravity and motion.

scientists to contribute significantly to knowledge about insects. He studied the flea, which he called "this minute and despised creature," in great detail. He described its anatomy and explained its metamorphosis. Many insects undergo *metamorphosis*—that is, different body forms—during their lifetime. He also clarified the life history of the ant. What people had thought to be ant eggs, Leeuwenhoek showed to be their pupae (a pupa is a stage in an insect's life). He identified the true ant eggs and showed that a larva (called a maggot) emerges from the egg.

Throughout his work with small organisms and insects, Leeuwenhoek opposed a popular belief known as spontaneous generation of life. According to this belief, some forms of life (such as bacteria and small insects) come into being out of nonliving matter, such as mud or rotting food. The theory of spontane-

ous generation claimed, therefore, that such forms of life do not come from reproduction by living organisms. Leeuwenhoek showed how organisms such as fleas, shellfish, and eels reproduce. He repudiated the idea that these particular animals generate spontaneously from nonliving matter. In combating this popular but wrongful notion, Leeuwenhoek proved himself a thinker ahead of his own time. Two hundred years would pass before Louis Pasteur would absolutely disprove spontaneous generation.

Anton Van Leeuwenhoek was born in Delft, a city in the Netherlands (Holland), in 1632. He probably had very little scientific education. As a young man, he became an apprentice to a linen cloth dealer in Amsterdam. Later he returned to Delft to establish his own clothing business. But in 1660, he obtained a city governmental position. This turn of events allowed Leeuwenhoek to devote a great deal of time to his hobby—grinding lenses and making observations with his microscopes.

Leeuwenhoek corresponded with the Royal Society of London over a period of 50 years. He was made a member of that English scientific society. Many of his discoveries were published in the journal of the Royal Society, the *Philosophical Transactions.*

Leeuwenhoek lived a long and fortunate life. His work was generally well received, and he became quite famous. Royal persons visited him, including Czar Peter the Great of Russia. Leeuwenhoek died at the age of 90 in 1723.

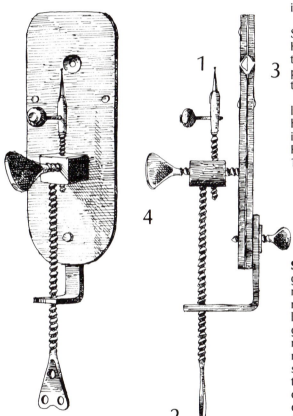

An engraving of one of van **Leeuwenhoek's** microscopes. The specimen was placed on the apparatus at (1), brought into position vertically by turning the lower screw (2), and moved to or away from the lens (3) by turning the shorter screw (4).

Sir Isaac Newton

Sir Isaac Newton (1642-1727) was one of the greatest scientists of all times. His theories on motion and gravity laid the foundations of modern physics. Until Albert Einstein published radical new theories on motion and gravity shortly after 1900, Newton's principles remained unchallenged. Even today, scientists realize that Newton's understanding of universal forces holds true in most situations. Newton determined the basic nature of light and color. The modern science of *optics,* the study of light and vision, developed from Newton's theories. Also, Newton discovered the form of

Nicolaus Steno, a Danish physician, formulated the law of superposition— that is, layers of rock are always deposited with the oldest strata on the bottom and the youngest on the top.

 1666

 1669

ca. 1670-1675

The Academy of Sciences is founded in Paris.

Jan Swammerdam publishes a treatise on metamorphosis of insects.

Anton Van Leeuwenhoek discovers microbes.

mathematics we now call *calculus.*

Like many scientists of his time, Newton wondered what forces keep the planets in orbits around the sun. Copernicus had first proposed the theory of a sun-centered solar system in the 1500's. Then, Johannes Kepler had worked out some—but not all—of the mathematical problems posed by the new theory. (Kepler had died about 10 years before Newton was born.) Newton tackled the difficult questions raised by the theories of Copernicus and Kepler.

Eventually, Newton was able to explain the motions of the planets in three basic laws:

(**1**) an object remains at rest until a force is applied to it (the principle of inertia);

(**2**) when a force is applied to an object, the change in that object's motion is proportional to the force;

(**3**) to every action there is an opposite and equal reaction.

Newton used these laws to help explain how the planets stay in their orbits around the sun. He developed a more general law stating that the force attracting planets to the sun decreases with the square of their distance from the sun. This law explains why the force attracting a planet to the sun keeps the planet in a regular orbit. The force is strong enough to keep the planet in its orbit, but not so strong that the planet is pulled into the sun, and not so weak that it flies away from the sun.

Newton carried these ideas further. He related the forces of planetary motion to other forces, such as the motion of the moon around the earth, and then to the motion of a falling object on the earth. He came to the conclusion that all of these motions are the result of a basic, universal force—the force of universal gravitation. Newton formulated a new law of universal gravitation, which states that every pair of bodies in the universe attracts each other. The force of attraction depends upon the *mass* of the objects (that is, the amount of matter they contain) and the distance between them.

Newton's law of universal gravitation explained how the universe is held together. For the first time in history, a complete, scientific explanation for the basic forces and interactions of forces in the universe had been made. In a sense, Newton's theories completed the work started by Copernicus. Copernicus introduced the idea that the universe is organized in a radically different way than previously believed. But Newton explained how this universe works.

Newton worked out these theories and wrote them down. However, he did not publish his work for many years. The English astronomer Edmond Halley stumbled upon Newton's great discoveries in 1684. Halley encouraged Newton to publish. Eventually, Halley paid all of the expenses, edited the work, and wrote a preface. The book, published as *Principia Mathematica* (Mathematical Principles of Natural Philosophy) in 1687, revolutionized science. Probably no one single publication has had as great an impact on science.

Within a generation or two of this publication, all of the university science positions in England were held by followers of Newton (called Newtonians). Before long, Newtonians dominated the universities of all Europe as well.

While working out his theories of gravitation, Newton had developed an entirely new branch of mathematics—calculus. *Calculus* provides the means to work out problems involving quantities that change continually. Calculus was an essential tool for solving some of the scientific problems that occupied thinkers of Newton's generation. Examples of these problems include motion, light refraction, and areas and volumes of complex figures. A German mathematician, Gottfried Leibniz, invented calculus independently of Newton, probably at a later time. But Leibniz published his work first. As a result, a furious feud developed between the two men. Newton maintained the feud until the end of his own life. Newton also made fundamental discoveries in the field of optics. In the years 1665-1666 Newton conducted experiments on light. From these experiments, he formed theories about the nature of light and color that helped shape modern science in these fields. Newton's work led him to reject the idea that white light is pure—that it cannot be divided into separate components or parts. The ancient Greek philosopher and scientist Aristotle had originally proposed just such a theory. But Newton showed that light can be separated into its separate parts (colors) by a prism. He claimed that white light is actually a mixture of these individual colors. Therefore, white light, rather than being pure and simple, is very complex. Later scientific analysis of light showed Newton's theory to be correct.

ca. 1678

Christian Huygens
formulates the wave theory
of light.

Newton also theorized that each type of light ray has unique, individual properties. And he believed that light rays are made of tiny particles, which he called *corpuscles*. Newton thus came amazingly close to the quantum theory of light—a theory that has been seriously developed only in our century.

Newton first published some of his ideas on light and colors in two papers for the Royal Society of London. His essay, "On Colors," appeared in 1672. In 1675 he published the essay, "An Hypothesis Explaining the Properties of Light." Newton published his entire body of theories on light in a book called *Opticks* in 1704. Interestingly, the second English edition of this work, published in 1717-1718, included Newton's first writings on his methods of calculus.

Newton's work in optics led him to develop a new kind of telescope, the reflecting telescope. A reflecting telescope uses mirrors to gather and focus light, rather than lenses. Newton felt the new technology was necessary because lenses produce *chromatic aberration.* This is a kind of distortion that results because light rays of different colors come to a focus on different focal planes.

Newton also devoted himself to the study of religion and theology. Like many English people of his time, Newton was strongly Protestant in his beliefs. But some of Newton's theological ideas went beyond the accepted doctrines of the Church of England and English society in general. For this reason, the several works that Newton wrote on theology were not published until after his death.

Isaac Newton was born in 1642 in a village in Lincolnshire, a part of England near the North Sea. Isaac's father died before the boy's birth, and his mother remarried while Isaac was quite young. Young Isaac was left in the care of his grandmother, while his mother went to live with her new husband's family. This separation lasted nine years.

Newton's early separation from his mother—and his hatred of the stepfather—emotionally scarred him for life. Although he lived for 84 years in relatively good physical health, Newton suffered several emotional breakdowns as an adult. He also cut himself off from his friends from time to time.

Eventually, Isaac's mother returned, widowed again. She sent him to school at Cambridge University, where Isaac received a BA degree in 1665. During the years 1665-1667, Cambridge was shut down because of a terri-

A 19th century, English engraving showing **Isaac Newton** analyzing a ray of light

ble plague epidemic—the last great epidemic of bubonic plague in England. In 1667 Newton returned to Cambridge as a teaching assistant, and in 1669 he became a full professor. During the plague years and the early years at Cambridge, Newton worked out many of his ideas on gravitation and optics.

In 1672 Newton was elected to the Royal Society of London. Newton was to publish many of his scientific theories through this organization. But Newton also got involved in terrible controversies with other society members. Some of his most famous controversies

Isaac Newton publishes his theories on gravitation and motion in *Principia Mathematica.*

 1687

were with Robert Hooke, who took issue with the ideas Newton published in his paper, "On Colors," in 1672. Later, Hooke claimed—falsely—that Newton had stolen some of his ideas to use in *Principia.* These criticisms drove Newton into rages. He seemed unable to accept criticism—or to separate valid, useful criticism from remarks meant to hurt him. On several occasions, Newton withdrew from the Royal Society and all of his friends after such an episode. Later in life, the quarrel with Leibniz over the invention of calculus led Newton to include harsh, bitter remarks in his writings. Newton continued such behavior even after the death of Leibniz.

In time, Newton moved away from the academic world and more into the political life of London. He supported the so-called "Glorious Revolution" of 1688-89, in which the Catholic king James II was replaced by the Protestant king and queen, William and Mary. In 1696 Newton was appointed warden of the mint, a public position that provided a large income. Newton performed his duties well, successfully trying and convicting many counterfeiters (criminals who print fake money).

The aging Newton came to be regarded as the "grand old man" of English science. He received many awards and honors. In 1699 Newton was elected to the French Academy of Science. In 1703 he was elected president of the Royal Society, a position he kept for the next quarter-century. Queen Anne made Newton a knight in 1705. Sir Isaac Newton was the first scientist to be honored in this way. In the following centuries, many more English scientists would be knighted or given titles of nobility. Sir Isaac Newton died in 1727.

Edmond Halley

Edmond Halley (1656-1742) was a prominent English astronomer who became famous for identifying the comet named after him and predicting its reappearance. But Halley made many other important contributions to astronomy and other sciences. Also, he had the good fortune to be part of a great scientific movement that included such scientists as Sir Isaac Newton and Robert Hooke.

Halley's first important work in astronomy

was in compiling a catalog of the stars seen in the Southern Hemisphere. In this task, Halley had been influenced by John Flamsteed, astronomer royal at the Royal Greenwich Observatory. Flamsteed used the telescope, then a rather new invention, to make an accurate catalog of stars seen in the Northern Hemisphere. Halley realized that an opportunity existed for a young astronomer like himself. At that time, all the centers of science were in the Northern Hemisphere—most in Europe. Halley decided to sail to the island of St. Helena in the South Atlantic. From that location, he could observe the southern stars. Halley returned to England and published his catalog of the southern stars in 1678. This work established his reputation as an astronomer.

Halley is most remembered for his studies of comets. In 1705 he published a book called *Synopsis of the Astronomy of Comets.* Halley described the orbits of a number of comets that had been sighted over the last few centuries. He concluded that the comets seen in 1531, 1607, and 1682 were so similar that they must in fact be the reappearance of a single comet. Based on this conclusion, Halley calculated that the comet would return in 1758. Events proved Halley's theory about the comet to be true, though he had died by the time of its reappearance. This comet was, of course, named Halley's Comet. It is the comet that reappeared in 1986.

Halley was involved in the scientific circle that included the great Isaac Newton. Halley discussed ideas with Newton and encouraged him in his work. Halley edited and published Newton's landmark book, the *Principia Mathematica,* in 1687. He also wrote a Latin preface for the book.

Halley enjoyed a wide range of scientific interests. He produced the first meteorological (weather) chart of the world, showing the prevailing winds, in 1686. In 1693, he published actuarial charts for the city of Dresden, Germany. An actuarial table shows statistical probabilities of life expectancy for a given population. This work laid the groundwork for modern insurance practices. In 1698-1700 Halley traveled on the first sea voyage taken for purely scientific reasons. From his observations on this voyage, Halley made the first magnetic charts of the Atlantic and Pacific oceans.

In later life, Halley determined an accurate way to measure the distance of the sun from

The Eighteenth Century——1700-1799

Isaac Newton publishes his discoveries in optics.

Daniel Bernoulli develops the kinetic theory of gases.

Joseph Black identifies carbon dioxide.

| 1704 | 1705 | ca. 1730 | 1751-1772 | ca. 1752 |

Edmond Halley publishes *Synopsis of the Astronomy of Comets,* in which he describes and accurately predicts the reappearance of the comet that will come to bear his name.

Diderot and **d'Alembert** publish a 28-volume encyclopedia, in which they catalog the science and technology of their day.

the earth. This measurement enabled scientists to determine the size of the solar system and the distances of other stars from the earth.

Edmond Halley was born in London and as a boy attended St. Paul's School in London. Later he studied at Oxford University. By 1678 Halley was recognized as an important astronomer and was elected to the Royal Society of London. From 1720 until his death, Halley served as astronomer royal at Greenwich.

Carolus Linnaeus

Carolus Linnaeus (1707-1778) was a Swedish naturalist and botanist who established the modern scientific system for naming and classifying living organisms. A born organizer, Linnaeus also suggested classification systems for minerals and for diseases.

Linnaeus developed a *binomial* system for classifying plants and animals. (Binomial means "having two names.") Each living organism has, at the very least, a *genus* name and a *species* name. A genus is a grouping of animals that are structurally similar. Also, according to evolutionary theory, animals in a genus evolved from a common ancestor. A species is a grouping of more closely related organisms. Under some conditions, organisms within a species might interbreed. (This would be impossible for organisms less closely related.) An example of a common binomial scientific name is *Homo sapiens,* the scientific name for human beings. *Homo* (meaning "man" in Latin) is the genus name. *Sapiens* ("wise" in Latin) is the species name. In scientific names, the genus name is usually written with an initial capital letter. The entire name appears in italic type, or it is underlined if in handwriting or typing.

Linnaeus published several books in which he set out his naming system for plants and animals. In *Species Plantarum* (1753), he described the system for plants. The tenth edition of *Systema Naturae* (1758) formulated the system for animals. The scientific naming system devised by Linnaeus proved extremely important to future scientific development. From this time, scientists could communicate without confusion about experiments and theories involving living organisms.

Linnaeus was born Carl von Linné in 1707. (The name *Linnaeus* was a Latin version of his given name. During the 1700's and before, many people used Latin forms of their names for professional purposes.) As a child, Carl was nicknamed "the little botanist" because of his interest in plants. As a young man, Linnaeus conducted a botanical expedition to Lapland, the far northern region of Scandinavia. He then went to the Netherlands, where he received his medical degree. Later, Linnaeus went to Holland—then the center for study of botany—to continue his studies. In 1738 Linnaeus returned to Sweden and established a medical practice. Eventually he was appointed professor of botany at the University of Uppsala.

Linnaeus was known in England, where his work was followed with interest. He had visited England in the 1730's. Shortly after Linnaeus died (in 1778), an Englishman, Sir J. E. Smith, purchased a large portion of the Swedish botanist's estate. This collection, including insect and shell collections, manuscripts, and a herbarium (dried plant collection), is still maintained by the Linnaen Society in London.

Henry Cavendish

Henry Cavendish (1731-1810) was an English physicist and chemist who made fundamental discoveries in a number of scientific fields, although several of them remained unpublished in his lifetime. Cavendish was exceptionally brilliant but highly eccentric as well. In fact, Cavendish probably fit some of the "mad scientist" stereotypes. He almost totally avoided contact with other people, spoke very little, and went about in shabby clothing. But Cavendish possessed one of the most brilliant minds and conducted some of the most original experiments of his age.

Cavendish did important experimental work in chemistry. He studied air and gases extensively. Cavendish was among the first scientists to recognize that hydrogen is a separate element. Experiments he conducted in 1784-1785 led Cavendish to the conclusion that water is a compound of hydrogen and air (oxygen). The chemist Joseph Priestley had done

Immanuel Kant, a German philosopher, suggests that the sun and planets were formed from the same elements and in the same way.

Henry Cavendish discovers properties of hydrogen.

1753	1755	1758	1766

Carolus Linnaeus publishes a fundamental treatise on plant classification.

Carolus Linnaeus publishes his treatise on animal classification.

the same experiments but had missed the importance of the water vapor produced when hydrogen and oxygen ignite. Cavendish also performed some experiments with carbon dioxide.

Cavendish made fundamental discoveries in electricity. He anticipated the work of several later scientists, but most of his work on electricity went unpublished for years. Almost a century later, the English physicist James Clerk Maxwell recovered Cavendish's findings, publishing some of them in 1879. Cavendish discovered the law of electricity that later became known as Coulomb's law (and Coulomb's discovery). This law states that the force of two electrical charges is inverse to the square of the distance between them. Cavendish anticipated Ohm's Law as well by observing that the electrical potential across two conductors is directly proportional to the current between them. Cavendish also discovered that all points on the surface of a good conductor are at the same potential with respect to the earth. This idea proved very important later in the development of electrical theory.

Cavendish had no instrument for measuring electrical current. He used his own body as a meter, grasping an electrode with each hand and then judging how far from his fingertips the shock spread.

Henry Cavendish was born in Nice, France, a descendant of the Duke of Devonshire and the Duke of Kent. He attended Cambridge University but did not obtain a degree. For many years, Cavendish lived with his father, also a distinguished scientist, in London. The two Cavendishes performed many experiments together. Henry's father died in 1783.

Henry Cavendish was elected to the Royal Academy in 1760. He became a foreign associate of the Institute of France in 1803. Cavendish possessed an enormous fortune, which he left to family members at his death in 1810. Many years later, in 1871, the Cavendish family endowed the Cavendish Laboratory at Cambridge, where many of the modern discoveries in physics have been made.

Henry Cavendish, English chemist and physicist, shown in an engraving after the drawing by Alexander

Joseph Priestley

Joseph Priestley (1733-1804) was one of the most original thinkers of the English-speaking world in the 1700's. Priestley made fundamental contributions to science. He discovered oxygen and about 10 other gases. He discovered basic principles of photosynthesis and conducted early experiments in electricity. Priestley was a freethinker in religion and a supporter of popular government, that is, government by the people.

Priestley's most famous achievement is his discovery of oxygen in 1774. (Actually, a Swedish chemist, Carl Scheele, discovered oxygen at about the same time as Priestley. Today, both scientists are given the credit.) Priestley called the substance "de-phlogisticated air." He took this name from a theory that was then current, but later proved false—the *phlogiston* theory. This theory stated that all flammable materials (those that will burn) contain a substance called phlogiston. (The *phl* letter group in *phlogiston* is pronounced like *fl.*) When a substance burns, it gives up its phlogiston to the air. Priestley knew that substances burn in the presence of oxygen. He therefore assumed that oxygen readily absorbs the phlogiston given off by the burning substances. According to his thinking, the oxygen originally contained no phlogiston. It was "dephlogisticated."

At about the same time, the great French chemist Antoine Lavoisier was conducting similar experiments. Priestley met Lavoisier in France in 1775. He gave Lavoisier detailed accounts of his experiments with the "de-phlogisticated" air. Lavoisier repeated Priestley's experiments. He recognized the true nature of the gas—that it was a basic chemical element—and gave it the name *oxygen.* He also discovered that oxygen combines chemically with other substances during combustion.

Priestley was a great experimenter who had talent for designing new laboratory devices when experiments required them. He was able to isolate, identify, and study a number of gases. These included nitrogen, nitric oxide, nitrogen dioxide, nitrous oxide (laughing gas), hydrogen chloride, ammonia, sulfur dioxide, silicon tetrafluoride, and carbon monoxide (a gas we know today as part of car exhaust fumes).

Priestley studied carbonation in liquids. He went to a beer factory and observed the bub-

David Rittenhouse builds a precise model of the solar system.

 1770

bles of carbon dioxide that develop in a fermenting liquid. Later Priestley developed a method for carbonating water. His work made possible the soda-water industry. (We use carbonated water today in products such as soft drinks and soda water.)

Priestley made some of the first important discoveries on plant photosynthesis. In photosynthesis, green plants use the sun's energy to change water and carbon dioxide into sugar, a basic food. Priestley discovered that green plants give off oxygen. He also noted that green plants need sunlight. Scientists studying photosynthesis in the late 1700's used these observations in their research.

Near the beginning of his scientific career, Priestley conducted experiments in electricity. He observed a relationship between electricity and chemical changes. Later, Priestley used an electric spark to decompose (break down) ammonia. This process is called *electrolysis.* Although Priestley is not credited with discovering electrolysis, his work paved the way for later discoveries. With the help of his friend, Benjamin Franklin, Priestley published in 1767 an important book on electricity. Entitled *The History and Present State of Electricity,* this book summed up the knowledge about electricity at that time and reported some of Priestley's own experiments. Very successful and popular, the book went into five editions.

Priestley also conducted experiments in optics, the study of light and vision. In 1772 he published his experimental findings and theories in a book called *History and Present State of Discoveries Relating to Vision, Light, and Colours.*

Joseph Priestley was born in Yorkshire (northeastern England) in 1733. His parents were *dissenters,* people who did not belong to the Church of England. Although England allowed some religious freedom at this time, dissenters were barred from many professions, schools, and universities.

Young Joseph Priestley entered Northampton Academy, a school run by dissenters, in 1752. There he received an excellent education. He trained to be a teacher and a minister.

Priestley was appointed a teacher at a dissenting academy in Warrington. While there he put many new ideas of education into practice. The dissenting schools had great freedom to develop curriculum (the course of study in a school) because the state church and the government were not involved. Priestley devel-

oped a new approach to teaching English grammar. He based his method on current English usage rather than models provided by the ancient classical languages (such as Greek and Latin). He also molded the school's curriculum to prepare students for careers in science, industry, the arts, and commerce. Under Priestley's influence, his academy became perhaps the best dissenting school in England. In recognition of his educational work, Priestley received an honorary doctoral degree from the University of Edinburgh, Scotland, in 1765.

During the 1760's, Priestley became friends with Benjamin Franklin, who was then serving in London. At about this time, Priestley began serious scientific experimentation. In 1766 Priestley was elected to the Royal Society of London.

Priestley's scientific career received a boost in 1772 when the Earl of Shelburn, a wealthy nobleman, became his patron. In return for tutoring the earl's children, Priestley received a salary and plenty of free time in which to experiment.

In 1779 Priestley left Shelburn's household to become minister to a dissenting congregation in Birmingham, England. During this period, Priestley wrote many theological works. He became more and more radical, rejecting many traditional Christian doctrines. He earned a controversial reputation as a freethinker for his religious and political opinions. When the French Revolution broke out in 1789, Priestley vocally supported it. Many local people became angry with Priestley because of his radical ideas. On July 14, 1791, a mob broke into Priestley's house, destroying everything, including his library and laboratory. Priestley and his family escaped Birmingham. Eventually, they emigrated to the United States.

In 1794 Priestley and his wife settled in Northumberland, Pennsylvania. There Priestley continued to write religious and political works. He became friends with John Adams and Thomas Jefferson. Both of these men admired Priestley's free spirit and intellect and agreed with many of his ideas. Joseph Priestley died in 1804.

1774

Joseph Priestley and **Carl Scheele** independently discover oxygen.

Antoine Lavoisier

Antoine Lavoisier (1743-1794) was a great French chemist who is often called the father of modern chemistry. Lavoisier was a scientist and thinker of unusually wide interests. He made contributions to many scientific fields. Lavoisier's brilliant scientific career was cut short by radicals of the French Revolution who had him executed by the guillotine in 1794.

Lavoisier's most important contribution to science was his explanation of the chemical basis of combustion (fire). He observed that when the chemical elements sulfur and phosphorus are burned, they increase in weight.

Lavoisier, the French chemist, shown in a 19th century etching and engraving

Lavoisier correctly assumed that these elements had combined chemically with air during combustion. Lavoisier did not know at that time, however, exactly what elements make up air. Then in 1774, Joseph Priestley of England discovered oxygen. (Priestley used a different name for the element; it is Lavoisier who coined the name "oxygen.") Lavoisier realized that this element—oxygen—combines with substances when they burn.

Lavoisier's theories led to the rejection of the *phlogistic doctrine,* which had been accepted as a basic principle of chemistry for many years. This doctrine claimed that all flammable materials (materials that will burn) contain a substance called *phlogiston.* (The *phl* letter-group in *phlogiston* is pronounced like *fl.*) When a substance burns, it gives up its phlogiston to the air, according to the theory. When Priestley discovered oxygen, for instance, he believed he had discovered "de-phlogisticated air." He knew that substances burn in the presence of oxygen. He therefore assumed that oxygen readily absorbs the phlogiston given off by the burning substances. This must mean that oxygen normally contains no phlogiston; therefore, it is "de-phlogisticated."

Lavoisier, however, understood that oxygen combines with substances during combustion. By weighing the matter before and after combustion, he was able to confirm this idea. Lavoisier's discovery was one of the most important in the history of chemistry. It led to another important discovery—that matter cannot be created or destroyed, only changed in form. This important principle is known as the law of conservation of matter.

Lavoisier developed a method for describing mathematically the chemical changes that matter can undergo. This method is the chemical equation. In a chemical equation, the mass of matter on the left side of the equation (before a chemical change) must equal the mass on the right side (after a chemical change). All chemists since Lavoisier's time have used the chemical equation in their work. Lavoisier also helped develop the system of chemical names now used.

Lavoisier also made the fundamental discovery that water is made of hydrogen and oxygen. Unknown to him, the English chemist Henry Cavendish had discovered this fact a short time earlier.

Lavoisier studied respiration in animals as a

Antoine Lavoisier gives the first accurate scientific explanation of combustion (fire).

1777

chemical process. He came to the conclusion that respiration is a kind of combustion. In respiration, oxygen is chemically combined with nutrients such as simple sugars. In this chemical reaction, heat is given off. Heat is a form of energy an organism must use to stay alive. Also, waste products such as carbon dioxide are given off. In describing respiration chemically, Lavoisier laid the foundation for modern biochemistry.

Lavoisier published his doctrines of chemistry in the *Elementary Treatise on Chemistry* in 1789. This became one of the most important early textbooks on chemistry. It also enabled other chemists to learn about Lavoisier's ideas.

Lavoisier was involved in public service for much of his adult life. This career gave Lavoisier many opportunities to apply his mathematical and scientific talents to practical uses. As a young man, he joined the geologist J. Guettard in a geological survey trip throughout France. Afterward, Lavoisier helped Guettard prepare a mineralogical atlas of France. He helped improve the manufacture of gunpowder. In agriculture, he established a model farm where principles of scientific agriculture were demonstrated. Also, Lavoisier served on the commission that devised the metric system, a uniform and scientific system of measurements. The French government adopted the metric system in 1795. Today it is used in most countries of the world and is the system of measurement used in science.

Antoine Lavoisier was born in 1743 of a well-to-do family in Paris. He received an excellent education. In 1766 young Lavoisier won a gold medal from the French Academy of Sciences for a plan of lighting city streets. Two years later he became a member of the Academy.

Lavoisier received a title of nobility in 1772. He also served in the French civil service, notably as a member of the nation's tax-collecting body. For these reasons, Lavoisier became the target of radical politicians who seized power in the early 1790's during the French Revolution. In 1792 Lavoisier was forced to leave his house and laboratory. In May, 1794, he was arrested and forced to stand trial. The revolutionaries made no effort to give Lavoisier a fair trial. He was convicted and condemned to death. Lavoisier was beheaded by the guillotine on May 8, 1794.

Sir William Herschel

Sir William Herschel (1738-1822) was a German-born British astronomer. Herschel is most well known as the discoverer of the planet Uranus in 1781. But Herschel also contributed to our understanding of nebulae and greatly expanded the number of nebulae and galaxies then known. Herschel was a builder of telescopes as well. Some of his telescopes were the largest and most powerful ever constructed to that time. They allowed Herschel to see more detail in the sky than nearly anyone else during his lifetime.

Herschel discovered the planet Uranus in 1781. News of the discovery—the first of a planet since prehistoric times—caused a sensation. Herschel became famous almost overnight. Within a year or so, Herschel had been elected to the Royal Society; he had received the Royal Society's Copley Medal; and he had been appointed astronomer to King George III. Along with this appointment came a guaranteed lifelong annual pension, which gave Herschel financial indeper.Jence. In his early forties, Herschel was now able to pursue astronomy as a full-time profession.

Herschel's greatest interest was the stars. He surveyed the skies repeatedly, looking for nebulae. A nebula (plural *nebulae*) is a hazy, cloudlike patch in the deep heavens. It is made of gases. Some nebulae reflect light; these appear as bright patches. Others absorb light and are, therefore, dark. They can only be seen in outline against brighter objects in the heavens.

In Herschel's time, astronomers sometimes confused nebulae with galaxies. Most of the telescopes then available could not resolve the images of the individual stars that make up a galaxy. For many years, Herschel thought that all nebulae were really galaxies. He expected that better telescopes would eventually resolve the "cloudy" image of nebulae into separate points of starlight. Then in 1790 Herschel observed a nebula in which a distinct star could be seen in the middle of the cloudy patch. This proved that the nebula was not simply a star cluster, for if it were, all or at least some of the stars should emerge in the image. Herschel concluded that a nebula is really a patch of "luminous fluid" out of which stars form.

Other observations of stars and star clusters led Herschel to develop theories about

Sir William Herschel discovers the planet Uranus.

Charles Coulomb formulates the laws of attraction and repulsion between electrically charged particles.

| 1781 | 1784-1785 | 1785 |

Henry Cavendish discovers that water is a chemical compound composed of hydrogen and oxygen.

the evolution of the universe. In this work, Herschel was a scientific pioneer. He noticed that stars tend to cluster together. Some clusters are more densely packed than others. Herschel suggested that all of the objects in the universe are gradually being drawn closer together by gravity. According to his theory, stars were rather evenly scattered at some earlier time in the universe. But now many clusters could be seen, some dense and some loose. With the passage of time, more and more separate, densely-packed star clusters would, according to Herschel, emerge. His later theory that stars form out of nebulae fit in well with these general star theories.

Over a 20-year period, Herschel cataloged 2,500 nebulae and star clusters. Before his work, only about 100 had been known. Herschel also cataloged 848 double-star pairs. He discovered that these are not random groupings of stars. Rather, the two stars in a star pair revolve around each other.

Herschel also discovered infrared rays. These are invisible light rays with greater wavelengths than visible light.

William Herschel was born in Hannover, Germany. As a young man not yet 20, Herschel fled to England during a French invasion of his homeland. He obtained work as a musician—teacher, performer, and composer. Herschel enjoyed a successful career in music until he was able to have a full-time career in astronomy in the 1780's.

William's sister Caroline had joined him in England. She became his loyal assistant and a fine astronomer in her own right. Caroline Herschel discovered several comets and nebulae. She also revised the catalog of nebulae and star clusters after her brother's death in 1822. For this work she received a gold medal from the Royal Astronomical Society in 1828. Rather late in life, William married a widowed neighbor, Mary Pitt. Mary also assisted him in his astronomical work. The Herschels had a son, John, who also became an astronomer. John Herschel extended his father's work with double stars. He received several scientific prizes for his work and was made a knight.

Herschel published 70 papers on a variety of topics in astronomy.

A drawing of **Volta's** "pile," or electric battery, made by Volta in an 1801 letter to de Dolomieu, a French geologist

Count Volta

Count Volta (1745-1827) was one of the most important early experimenters in electricity. Volta discovered constant-current electricity and made the first battery.

Volta experimented with electricity for many years. His understanding of several important principles of electricity led him to the invention of the *voltaic pile,* the first battery. Volta understood that different metals have different potentials for gaining a negative or positive charge of particular strength. He also knew that some chemicals, when dissolved in water, become powerful conductors of electricity called *electrolytes.*

Volta conducted a search of metals to find the pairing that would produce the greatest difference in charge. This work led to the earliest form of the *electromotive series,* a ranking of metals according to potential electrical charge. After many tests, Volta settled on zinc

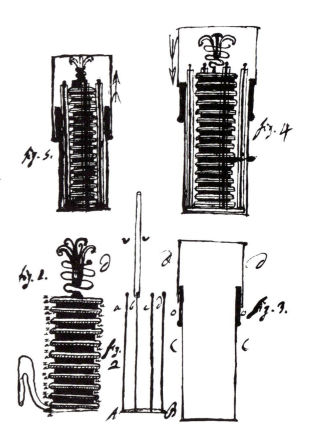

Antoine Lavoisier publishes the first modern textbook on chemistry.

1789

ca. 1791-1796

Benjamin Banneker, an American astronomer and mathematician, publishes a series of almanacs that include his own astronomical and tidal calculations.

and silver as the best pairing to generate a wide difference in charge.

Next, Volta built his electrical "pile." He stacked a zinc disk on top of a silver disk. On top of this pair, Volta placed a cloth that had been soaked with salt solution, an electrolyte. Volta repeated the same stacked layers a number of times. He believed that the difference in charge between the zinc and silver disks would become additive in the pile. In other words, the individual charges would be added together to make a much greater total charge. Volta's assumption proved correct. When he connected the voltaic pile in an electrical circuit, the pile caused current to flow. Volta reported his invention to the scientific world in the *Philosophical Transactions* of the Royal Society of London in 1800.

Using his voltaic pile, Volta chemically decomposed water with an electric current. That is, he broke down the water molecules into their separate components—hydrogen and oxygen. This experiment opened the way for the science of electrochemistry.

In other scientific experiments, Volta discovered and isolated methane gas around the year 1778.

Count Volta was born Alessandro Volta in Cuomo, Italy, in 1745. He taught physics at Cuomo and then, for many years, at the University of Pavia, in Italy.

Volta was made a foreign member of the Royal Society of London in 1791. He won the society's most valued honor, the Copley Medal, in 1794.

The French emperor, Napoleon I, heard of Volta's experiments with the voltaic pile and invited him to Paris in 1801. Volta performed experiments before members of the Institute of France and won many honors. A gold medal was struck in his honor, and the French government gave him a large grant of money. Napoleon gave Volta the title of *count,* a rank of nobility.

Count Volta died in 1827. Science has honored him by using the term *volt* as the standard unit of electromotive force.

Benjamin Banneker

Benjamin Banneker (1731-1806), an astronomer, mathematician, inventor, and compiler of almanacs, was one of the first important black intellectuals in the United States. During the 1790's, Banneker produced a yearly almanac in which he published his own astronomical and tide calculations. Thomas Jefferson became aware of Banneker's achievements and sent a copy of Banneker's almanac to the Royal Academy of Sciences in Paris. Primarily through Jefferson's interest, Banneker became widely known in England and the United States, especially among abolitionists in both countries.

Banneker was born a free black in Maryland. Largely self-taught, Banneker possessed a brilliant intellect. As an example of his inventiveness, Banneker built a wooden clock with hand-carved, movable parts, using only a pocket watch and a picture of a clock as models. The clock kept time for more than 50 years.

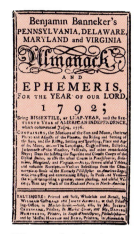

Title page of **Benjamin Banneker's** 1792 *Almanac,* published in Baltimore

Edward Jenner

Edward Jenner (1749-1823), an English physician, discovered a vaccination for smallpox and worked hard to make it generally available. Throughout much of history, smallpox had been widely dreaded. When sick with smallpox, a person breaks out in sores all over the body, rather like the sores caused by chicken pox. But smallpox is much more serious than chicken pox, very often causing the sick person to die or badly scarring the skin if he or she survives. Before vaccination, outbreaks of smallpox often caused hundreds or thousands of people to sicken and die in a short time.

By the 1700's, people realized that if a person is infected—that is, becomes sick—with smallpox once, that person can never get the disease again. For this reason, people sometimes allowed themselves to be infected with material taken from the sore of a smallpox patient. This could be done by making a small cut in the skin of the healthy person and putting the smallpox material directly on the cut. The person receiving the smallpox *inoculation,* as this practice is called, expected to get sick. The hope was that a case of smallpox

Woodcut of **Benjamin Banneker,** originally published on the cover of Banneker's 1795 *Almanac*

Count Alessandro Volta builds the first electric battery—the voltaic pile.

Edward Jenner gives the first successful vaccination—for smallpox.

ca. 1792-1795   1796

Pierre Simon de Laplace, a French mathematician, proposes that the sun and planets were formed from a spinning cloud of gas called a nebula.

caught in this way would be mild. The inoculation sometimes backfired, however. The person might get a very bad case of smallpox, perhaps even leading to death. Also, the inoculated person, once infected, could spread deadly smallpox to others.

Edward Jenner was practicing medicine in a rural area of England in 1796. As a doctor, he treated many cases of smallpox. Jenner wanted to find a way to stop the human suffering and death that this dreaded disease always brought. The people in his community, a rural market town, believed that a person who had been infected with cowpox could not catch smallpox. They had noticed that dairymaids (women who milk cows) seemed to stay

"The First Vaccination by **Doctor Jenner,**" a 19th century painting by Mélingue

healthy during smallpox epidemics. They knew that dairymaids often caught cowpox—a disease that is like smallpox but much milder—from the cows. It seemed that cowpox somehow protected dairymaids from smallpox.

Jenner believed that scientific principles lay behind this rural wisdom. He planned an experiment that would test the cowpox theory. In May, 1796, Jenner found a dairymaid who had cowpox sores on her hand. He took some material from one of the sores on her hand. Then he made shallow cuts on the arm of an eight-year-old boy. He applied the cowpox material from the dairymaid's sore directly on the boy's cuts. In a short time, the boy developed a low fever and a sore. This proved that he had been infected with the cowpox. Forty-eight days later, Jenner repeated the procedure, using smallpox matter instead. The boy stayed healthy. The first true vaccination ever given had proved successful.

Jenner made several more tests before he published his discovery of a smallpox vaccination. Although he had strong evidence of the vaccination's success, gaining public acceptance proved difficult. In 1797 the Royal Society refused to publish a paper he submitted. Jenner, therefore, published his own book the next year, *Inquiry into the Causes and Effects of the Variolae Vaccinae*. Also, Jenner enlisted the help of some London physicians to vaccinate patients. Gradually, the medical profession and the public accepted Jenner's vaccination and acknowledged that the English country doctor had made a great medical breakthrough. By 1800 and afterward, smallpox vaccination was being used widely, not only in England, but in Europe and America as well. Eventually it reached into most regions of the world.

Known today mostly for his work with the smallpox vaccination, Edward Jenner was recognized as a talented medical researcher in his own day. He understood the importance of experimentation and followed strictly scientific principles in his experiments. Jenner was also a popular, well-liked country doctor in his home county of Gloucestershire.

Edward Jenner was born in Berkeley in southwestern England in 1749. This is the community in which he spent most of his adult life as a practicing doctor. At the age of 13, Edward became an apprentice to a local surgeon. Apprenticeship, a practice in which a young person learns a craft or trade from a skilled adult, was common in medicine at that time. Young Edward learned a great deal about medicine in the eight years of his apprenticeship.

At the age of 21, Edward Jenner went to London to study medicine with John Hunter, a widely respected doctor. This was the beginning of an important friendship and professional relationship. Hunter encouraged scientific curiosity and discipline in his pupil. Under Hunter's influence, Jenner developed skills and practices that would help in his work with smallpox vaccination. Jenner suffered a great personal loss when John Hunter died in 1793.

Jenner returned to medical practice in Berkeley after two years of study with Hunter in London. He enjoyed a successful and popular practice. He married in 1788.

Jenner enjoyed a wide range of interests. He especially loved nature. Living in a rural area, he found many opportunities to study and enjoy nature. At that time, Gloucestershire was untouched by the industrial growth then occurring elsewhere in England. He observed the migration and nesting habits of birds. He also collected specimens of birds, animals, and plants. Other hobbies Jenner enjoyed were playing the violin and writing poetry.

Jenner's work with smallpox changed his way of life. From 1796, he spent much of his time developing and promoting the smallpox vaccination. Most of his efforts earned him no income. The British Parliament voted him grants of money in 1802 and 1806 to acknowledge and honor his great achievement.

After his wife's death in 1815, Edward Jenner retired from medical practice. He died in 1823.

Baron Georges Cuvier, the French naturalist, studies fossils in a painting by Chartran

Baron Cuvier

Baron Cuvier (1769-1832), a French naturalist, pioneered in several scientific fields and wrote important early texts on the study of animals. Cuvier's work in comparative anatomy—the comparative study of the body structures of animals—and in paleontology—the study of fossil records—set these developing sciences on firm foundations.

Cuvier gained considerable skill dissecting and describing animals at a young age. He conducted studies of sea animals, particularly mollusks—animals such as oysters, clams, squids, and octopuses—and wrote notes on his findings. Later he dissected large animals, such as the rhinoceros and elephant.

Cuvier's study of a wide variety of animal life led him to some important conclusions. He formulated a principle which he called "corre-

Early Nineteenth Century——1800-1849

○ ca. 1800-1805

Baron Cuvier develops a system of classifying animals according to body types; he establishes the science of comparative anatomy.

lation of parts." The principle states that the structure of every organ in an animal body is functionally related to the structure of all other body parts. Furthermore, Cuvier stated that the structures of animal body parts result from the animal's functions and habits. This opinion put him in direct conflict with certain other naturalists, who believed that body structures predetermine an animal's way of life.

In the meantime, Cuvier's anatomical studies led him into systematic study of fossils. He reconstructed skeletons of unknown four-legged animals from fossil finds. These efforts provided evidence that whole species of animals had become extinct during the earth's history. Cuvier also made careful observations about the layers of rock from which characteristic fossil types were taken. He concluded that the deeper, more distant layers contain fossil remains less like living animals than layers closer to the surface.

During Cuvier's lifetime, argument raged in Europe over the issue of the evolution of life. The argument would continue among scientists until general acceptance of Charles Darwin's theory of evolution in the later 1800's. Cuvier rejected a theory of evolution. He believed that animal body parts were so well designed and coordinated that any evolutionary changes would have led to extinction of the animals. To explain his extraordinary discoveries in the fossil records, Cuvier promoted the theory of "catastrophism"—that is, a theory claiming that sudden drastic changes in the earth had led to the extinction of some animals and shaped the earth's surface. This theory was later discounted by geological evidence that changes in the earth's surface occur over vast stretches of time.

Cuvier also developed strong opinions on the proper classification of animals. He identified four large animal groups, each of which had a number of similarities in terms of body structures. In this work, he took issue with many contemporary naturalists who believed that animals should be classified linearly—that is, in a straight line from the simplest organism up to human beings. Though Cuvier's particular system is not used today, his idea that animals should be classified in distinct groups according to anatomy is accepted. Later, Darwin's theories would claim that groups of animals with similar anatomy have descended from a common ancestor.

Cuvier was born in France and lived most

of his life in that country, though he studied comparative anatomy in Stuttgart, Germany, as a youth. In 1795 he joined the staff of the Museum of Natural History in Paris. There he gained the friendship and support of Étienne Geoffroy Saint-Hilaire, a professor of zoology at the museum. Eventually the two men's views grew apart. Their differences led to a famous public debate on animal classification at the Academy of Sciences in 1830. In addition to his scientific pursuits, Cuvier also served in the French government on several occasions.

Baron Cuvier wrote a number of important scientific treatises. These include *The Animal Kingdom* (1817), a fundamental textbook on zoology, *Elementary Survey of the Natural History of Animals* (1797), *Lessons on Comparative Anatomy* (1800-05), and *Discourse on the Revolutions of the Globe* (1825). In the latter work, Cuvier set out his conclusions about the earth's development and history, drawn from his observations of fossils.

John Dalton

John Dalton (1766-1844) was a highly original English scientist who studied a wide range of topics in science. Dalton is best known, however, for his contributions to the atomic theory of matter.

The atomic theory proposes that all matter is made up of very tiny particles called atoms. Dalton refined the theory by suggesting that each chemical element consists of a single type of atom. Although an amount of the element may contain many, many atoms, they are all identical in size, shape, and mass. Furthermore, Dalton theorized that in a chemical compound, the atoms of the different elements always combine in the same ratio. These ideas contributed to scientific understanding of the nature of matter. Later physicists and chemists would build on Dalton's theories.

In a similar vein, Dalton arranged all of the known chemical elements in a table according to atomic weight. (Dalton understood that each element has a unique atomic weight, since the atoms of each element are unique.) Dalton's table was a very early version of the periodic table developed in the later 1800's by Dmitri

John Dalton develops an atomic theory of chemical elements.

1803

Mendeleev and others. Dalton also devised a system of chemical symbols to use in formulas.

Dalton made fundamental contributions to the scientific understanding of gases. He first stated the law of partial pressures. This law explains that the total pressure in a mixture of gases equals the sum of the pressure exerted independently by each gas. It is now called Dalton's law. Another chemical law credited to Dalton states that a gas expands as it is heated. (This law is now called Charles' law—even though Dalton really discovered it first.) Furthermore, Dalton proved that gases dissolve in water. He also proved the rate of diffusion of gases.

Early in life, Dalton developed a strong interest in meteorology, the scientific study of weather. He was one of the first people to study weather from a scientific viewpoint. Dalton kept a diary on weather conditions in his native region—the Lake District of northwestern England. His diary eventually contained 200,000 entries—a treasure of weather data for future meteorologists.

Dalton confirmed that rain falls when the temperature of a cloud declines, not because of a drop in atmospheric pressure. He also developed a theory to explain the cause of the trade winds, which occur in the latitudes of the earth near the equator. Dalton said that the trade winds were caused by a combination of the earth's rotation and temperature variations in the earth's atmosphere. Dalton studied the aurora borealis—an occasional brilliant, shimmering display of lights in the northern skies. He concluded that the earth's magnetism was at least part of the cause of the aurora. Later scientific findings proved Dalton largely correct in these theories.

Dalton also investigated the condition in some human males known as color blindness. John and his brother had this condition, in which a person fails to perceive colors accurately. Dalton published his results. Because of this work, the condition of color blindness is also known as *Daltonism.*

John Dalton was born in northern England in 1766 of Quaker parents. His father was a weaver. With little formal education, Dalton began teaching in a Quaker school while still a boy. At that time, few standards for teaching existed. Moreover, public education was not available, and teachers were few.

Later Dalton became a science and mathematics teacher at New College in Manchester. A Presbyterian school, the New College admitted Quakers, while the great English universities at Cambridge and Oxford admitted only members of the Church of England.

In 1800 Dalton became secretary of the Manchester Literary and Philosophical Society. He later became its president. Dalton made many of his scientific research and discoveries known through this scientific society. He also kept notes for the society, which proved valuable to later scientists. Unfortunately, these documents were destroyed in German bombing raids on England during World War II.

Dalton lived a quiet, mostly solitary, life. He never married. He remained a faithful Quaker throughout his life, always wearing the simple clothing of a Quaker.

A member of the Royal Society, Dalton received a Gold Medal in 1826. He was also a corresponding member of the French Academy of Sciences and a founding member of the British Association for the Advancement of Science. John Dalton died in 1844.

Sir Humphry Davy

Sir Humphry Davy (1778-1829), an English chemist, isolated several chemical elements, discovered certain chemical compounds, and conducted experiments in electrochemistry. A gifted theoretical and experimental scientist, Davy frequently applied scientific knowledge to practical problems, most notably as the inventor of the miner's safety lamp. An admired lecturer, Davy popularized science in the British Isles as well as in Europe.

Davy analyzed the workings of a voltaic cell, the main component of an electrical battery. He became convinced that a voltaic cell produces electricity from a chemical reaction, specifically the chemical combination of two substances having opposite charges. From this conclusion, he reasoned that electrolysis could be used to break down chemical compounds into basic chemical elements. Electrolysis is the use of electric current to cause chemical reactions in certain substances.

Davy's conclusion proved correct. Using electrolysis, he isolated the elements sodium and potassium from their compounds in 1807.

Amadeo Avogadro formulates the theory that equal volumes of all gases at the same temperature and pressure contain equal numbers of particles.

1807

1811

Humphry Davy isolates the elements sodium and potassium.

In 1808 he isolated the alkaline-earth metals, a group of chemical elements including calcium, magnesium, barium, and strontium. He also discovered the element boron. Davy was the first scientist to recognize that diamonds are a form of carbon.

Davy studied the common chemical compound, hydrochloric acid. He realized that chlorine is a part of hydrochloric acid but failed to understand that chlorine is a chemical element. He explained in chemical terms how bleach works (by releasing oxygen from water, a hydrogen-oxygen compound). In later chemical researches, Davy studied iodine (which he called *substance X*) and showed its similarity to chlorine. Development of the periodic table of elements some years later would show iodine and chlorine to be closely related, lining up in the table in the same column.

Davy examined the relationship between electricity and magnetism. These researches probably influenced his assistant, Michael Faraday, who was destined to become one of the leading scientists in the fields of electricity and magnetism.

Sir Humphry Davy also discovered a number of practical uses of science. Davy perfected a miner's safety lamp in 1815, an invention that greatly reduced the risks of mine explosions. For this invention and related researches, he won the Rumford gold and silver medals from the Royal Society and a gift of silver from the northern mine owners. In studies of leather tanning processes, Davy found a substance in tropical plants that could be used much more cheaply than oak extracts, which had been used up to that time. He also experimented with electrochemical methods to prevent saltwater corrosion of a ship's copper sheathing. Although his theory was correct, Davy never produced practical results in this effort, which he had begun late in life.

Humphry Davy was born in Penzance, England, of middle-class parents. As a youth he was apprenticed to a surgeon-pharmacist. (The medical professions were not clearly defined in the late 1700's.) This experience may have spurred the youngster's scientific interests. The young Davy also expressed interest in becoming a poet, but science won out.

In 1798 Davy was appointed chemical superintendent at the Pneumatic Institution. This was his first real position as a scientist. In 1802 Davy became professor of chemistry at the Royal Institution of Great Britain, then new.

Davy's growing reputation at a young age is confirmed by his admission in 1803 to the Royal Society and in the same year to the Dublin Society (as an honorary member).

The Davys travelled in France during 1813-1815 with the permission of Napoleon and were presented to the empress Marie Louise. In 1812 Davy was made a knight. Davy served as president of the Royal Society, a position of great prestige, from 1820 until 1827. Throughout his professional career, Davy was widely admired and popular as a lecturer and supporter of science.

Davy was an individual of extremely wide interests. He wrote poetry and enjoyed the friendship of poets and writers including Samuel Taylor Coleridge. An amateur naturalist, he loved nature and wandering through the English countryside. The sport of fishing was his passionate hobby. Near the end of his life, Davy wrote and partially illustrated a book about fishing. Davy's varied interests often carried over into his scientific projects. While vacationing in Italy, he studied volcanoes and attempted (unsuccessfully) to unroll papyrus scrolls that had been found at Herculaneum, one of the towns buried by volcanic material from Mount Vesuvius in ancient times.

Davy produced a number of written works, some of them printed versions of his many popular lectures. His published account of the tanning process he had developed served as the tanning industry's chief guide for many years. A chemistry textbook, *Elements of Chemical Philosophy,* was published in part but never finished. This work received high praise from J.J. Berzelius, the great contemporary Swedish chemist. Davy's book on fishing, *Salmonia: or Days of Fly Fishing,* was published in 1828. A book of dialogues called *Consolations in Travel, or the Last Days of a Philosopher* was published after Davy's death, in 1830.

Jöns Jacob Berzelius

Jöns Jacob Berzelius (1779-1848), a Swedish scientist, is one of the founders of modern chemistry. Berzelius made a number of important discoveries and developed basic practices and analytical techniques used in modern chemistry.

Jöns Jacob Berzelius published his study of atomic weights of elements, using oxygen as a standard against which others are measured.

1818

Berzelius made a careful study of atomic weights of elements, using oxygen as a standard against which other elements could be measured. His findings, first published in 1818 and revised in 1826, reveal a remarkable degree of accuracy. This important work contributed to the later development of the modern atomic theory. Berzelius also discovered several elements, including cerium, selenium, and thorium. He isolated the elements silicon, zirconium, and titanium. Working in an improvised kitchen laboratory, Berzelius developed modern laboratory techniques, including the water bath, desiccator, rubber tubing, wash bottle, and filter paper. He is also credited with originating the system of writing chemical symbols and formulas.

Berzelius was born in Götland, Sweden. Despite nearly failing his medical studies at the University of Uppsala, Berzelius received an M.D. degree in 1802 and was made full professor at the same university in 1807. The following year he was elected to the Stockholm Royal Academy of Science. Later Berzelius became a professor of chemistry at the Royal Caroline Meidoc-Chirugical Institute in Stockholm.

Berzelius published many scientific papers and a textbook on chemistry that was highly popular in its time and influential in the scientific community.

Hans Christian Oersted

Hans Christian Oersted (1777-1851) was a Danish scientist who discovered the principle of electromagnetism. In 1820, Oersted noticed that the needle of a compass jumps when the compass is placed near a wire carrying electric current. From this observation, Oersted concluded that an electric current produces a magnetic field. Oersted was the first person to notice the connection between electricity and magnetism. His discovery led to a rapid chain of discoveries in the fields of electricity and magnetism within a few years. Michael Faraday, Joseph Henry, and André-Marie Ampère all carried out important work in these related fields.

Oersted was probably the first scientist to isolate the element aluminum. This he did,

though in an impure form, in 1825. Oersted also conducted research into gases and fluids.

Hans Oersted was born in Rudkøbing, Denmark, in 1777. He received a doctoral degree from the University of Copenhagen, Denmark, in 1799. He taught chemistry and physics at that university for many years. Oersted died in 1851. Oersted was honored by having a standard physical unit of measurement named for him. The *oersted* is a measure of the strength of a magnetic field caused by electric current flowing through a wire.

André-Marie Ampère

André-Marie Ampère (1775-1836), a French physicist, discovered the laws of electromagnetism, founding the modern science of electromagnetism (which he named *electrodynamics*). Ampère made his fundamental discoveries in the 1820's, spurred by the Danish physicist Hans Oersted's 1820 observation that a magnetic needle is deflected when placed near a wire-carrying current. Ampère's own experiments showed that parallel electric currents moving in the same direction attract each other, while those moving in opposite directions repel each other. From these and similar observations, Ampère developed a mathematical theory that describes the relationship of a magnetic field to the electric current that produces it. This theory has come to be known as *Ampère's law*.

A further discovery led to the invention of the galvanometer, an instrument for measuring electric current. Ampère found that applying an electric current to a coiled wire makes the wire behave like a magnet. He used this scientific principle to develop the galvanometer.

Ampère was a child prodigy who had mastered mathematics by early adolescence and was made a full professor at the age of 26. Later, in 1809, he became professor of mathematics at the École Polytechnique in Paris. Throughout his life, Ampère's scientific approach was to follow a flash of inspiration and work to a conclusion rather than to work methodically.

Ampère published his fundamental work on electromagnetism, *Mathematical Theory of*

André Ampère discovers the basic laws of electromagetism.

1820

ca. 1822

1826

Hans Oersted discovers the magnetic field surrounding a conductor carrying an electric current.

Joseph Niepce produces the first photograph.

Electrodynamic Phenomena, in 1827. Science honors Ampère by the name for the standard unit of electric current measurement, the *ampere.*

Robert Brown

Robert Brown (1773-1858) was a Scottish physician and botanist who made several fundamental scientific discoveries. Brown discovered the nucleus in living cells. Later he described the agitation of microscopic particles that became known as Brownian motion. Brown noticed that a substance in which particles are constantly undergoing tiny fluctuations of movement behaves in predictable ways. Generally, the particles gradually spread from areas of greater concentration to areas of lesser concentration, causing the motion to "even out" in the substance. Brown observed these effects in pollen grains, but eventually the principle was applied to many other scientific areas, including chemistry and physics.

Robert Brown held wide scientific interests. At one time he served as curator of the British Museum. For five years, he explored Australia and Tasmania for botanical specimens. He also did important pioneering work in the study of plant fossils.

Friedrich Wöhler

Friedrich Wöhler (1800-1882) was a great German chemist. Wöhler made important contributions to chemistry as a researcher, teacher, and writer. He is most remembered, however, as the first person to synthesize (make) an organic compound in the laboratory.

In 1828 Wöhler synthesized the substance *urea* in his laboratory from another chemical. Urea is an organic compound, that is, a chemical compound based on carbon and made in nature only by living things. He was the first person ever to synthesize an organic compound from an inorganic one. Wöhler's achievement settled a great controversy among scientists. Many scientists believed in a

theory called "vital force." According to this theory, many of the processes that take place in living organisms—including chemical functions—were thought to be caused by the vital, or life, force. Therefore, they could not be analyzed according to the same scientific, experimental principles as processes in the physical world. Wöhler's synthesis of urea showed the falseness of the vital force theory. His work paved the way for the field of organic chemistry. Today, chemists can synthesize thousands of organic compounds in the laboratory.

Wöhler investigated many other organic compounds. Working with another German chemist, Justus von Liebig, he discovered the radical, benzoyl. A radical is a cluster of atoms that passes unchanged through many chemical changes. It serves as the root of many related organic compounds. (Radical means "root" in Latin.) No one had known of the existence of radicals before Wöhler and von Liebig.

Wöhler and von Liebig attempted to develop a theory to explain the structure of organic compounds. But another German chemist, Friedrich Kekulé von Stradonitz, actually laid the theoretical foundations of organic chemistry.

Wöhler also did research on a number of inorganic substances. He isolated the element aluminum in its metallic form. The method he used in this work was later developed into an industrial process. Wöhler himself developed a process that could be used in factories to produce large quantities of nickel. He isolated (and named) a new chemical element, beryllium, in 1828. Wöhler did experiments on compounds of silicon, adding considerably to our knowledge of this element. He thus indirectly influenced the computer industry of today. (Computer chips are made from silicon.)

Wöhler was well-liked and respected as a great teacher and lecturer of his time. From 1836, he was professor at the University of Göttingen, a city in central Germany. There he attracted a large following of students, both for his fine lectures and his concern for students.

Wöhler contributed many writings to the field of chemistry. He translated the works of the great chemist Jöns Jacob Berzelius from Swedish into German. Wöhler had studied with Berzelius as a young man. Wöhler wrote important textbooks in organic, inorganic, and

Robert Brown described the agitation of microscopic particles, now known as Brownian motion.

 1827

 1828

Georg Ohm discovers the fundamental law of current electricity that comes to bear his name.

Friedrich Wöhler synthesizes the organic substance urea from inorganic materials.

analytical chemistry. For many years, he edited the important German chemistry journal, *Annals of Chemistry.* This journal is still published today.

Friedrich Wöhler was born in 1800 in Eschersheim, a small German village. He attended the universities of Marburg and Heidelberg (both cities are now in West Germany). He earned a degree in medicine in 1823. In the same year, he went to Sweden to study with Berzelius, recognized as the greatest chemist in Europe at that time. Wöhler returned to Germany in 1825, teaching at Berlin and later at Kassel, in central Germany.

In 1832 Wöhler went to the German town of Giessen to work with Justus von Liebig, who was then known widely as a great chemist. Here, Wöhler did some of his most important work. In 1836 Wöhler was appointed professor of chemistry at the University of Göttingen. There he remained for the rest of his life.

An 1860 photograph of **Michael Faraday,** the English chemist and physicist

Michael Faraday

Michael Faraday (1791-1867), an English chemist and physicist, made very important contributions to scientific knowledge of electricity and magnetism. His work helped make possible the development of electrical power. Moreover, Faraday's theories on electricity and magnetism established the basis for more complete theoretical understanding of these forces. Faraday also made important discoveries in chemistry. Only a handful of scientists in the 1800's made as great an impact on later developments in science and technology as Faraday.

As a young man, Faraday served as assistant to Sir Humphry Davy, the great chemist. Eventually, Faraday made important chemical discoveries on his own. He isolated benzene, an organic compound, and described its molecule. He was the first to synthesize compounds out of the elements carbon and chlorine.

In the 1820's, however, Faraday turned his attention to electricity and magnetism. These topics became the scientific passion of his life. Faraday is most remembered for his work with them. Two physicists had made important discoveries about electricity in the early 1820's. Physicist Hans Christian Oersted, a Dane, dis-

covered that electrical current flowing through a wire produces a magnetic field around the wire. Then, French physicist André-Marie Ampère found that the magnetic field produced in this way is circular. As a result, the field around a current-carrying wire has the shape of a cylinder. A cylinder is a type of circular shape in space, like a can or a tube.

Faraday extended this understanding of electricity and magnetism. He speculated that a magnetic pole would move constantly in a circular path through the electromagnetic field around a current-carrying wire. Faraday proved this idea experimentally. He developed a device in which a magnet is left free at one end to rotate around a wire when current is applied. Faraday's experiment worked as he had suspected—and also demonstrated for the first time the principle of the electric motor.

Faraday's next important discovery—of electrical induction—came in 1831. When a current is started in a wire, the process is called electromagnetic induction. Faraday found that the current could be started, or *induced,* by moving a magnet in and out of a coil of wire. This

Robert Brown discovers the nucleus in living cells.

 1831

Michael Faraday and **Joseph Henry** independently discover the principle of electromagnetic induction.

principle is the basis of all electrical generators. An American physicist, Joseph Henry, had independently made the same discovery several months earlier. But Faraday published his results first.

Faraday had a strong interest in the theoretical aspects of science. He was dissatisfied with making such discoveries as electromagnetic induction without also understanding the underlying physics. To this end he devoted much of his scientific career. Although he never completely worked out electromagnetic theory, his ideas deeply influenced later physicists.

Many scientists of Faraday's time thought that electricity is a liquidlike substance that flows through wires just as water flows through pipes. Faraday, however, gradually developed radically different ideas. He believed that electricity was caused by build-up of tension or strain in matter. The tension increases to a breaking point; then it is passed outward from the source. The build-up and release of tension occurs in rapid cycles, and tension is distributed in waves. Later scientific understanding would show Faraday's concept of electrical current to be remarkably accurate.

In later life, Faraday further refined these ideas. He theorized on the way force fields—such as those created by electricity, magnetism, or gravity—work in space that is not occupied by matter. These ideas laid the groundwork for later development of field theory, which considers the nature of force fields. James Clerk Maxwell, a British physicist active in the later 1800's, developed these ideas mathematically.

Faraday's experimental work in electricity also led to important discoveries in electrochemistry. He discovered the mathematical relationship between electricity and the *valence,* that is, the combining power, of a chemical element. Faraday's law states this relationship. It gave the first clue to the existence of electrons.

Michael Faraday was born in 1791 in a country village in Surrey, England. He came from a rather poor family. The Faradays belonged to a small Protestant religious group called the Sandemanians. The strict, simple piety of Faraday's childhood deeply affected his thinking throughout life.

Though little opportunity was available to the child of a rural, poor blacksmith at that time, young Michael managed to get a job with a bookbinder. This proved a fortunate

turn of fate, because the work enabled Faraday to get books to read. During this time, Faraday came upon a book about electricity. Thus began his lifelong interest in electricity. Unable to afford higher education, the teen-ager set up his own crude laboratory and conducted experiments.

The second great stroke of fortune in Faraday's youth was to become acquainted with the chemist Sir Humphry Davy. A combination of Faraday's own persistent efforts and good luck led to his appointment as Davy's assistant in 1813. Faraday was a little over 20 years old at the time. This marked the beginning of a long, productive scientific career for the young man. In addition to his experimental work, Faraday became one of the most popular lecturers of his day.

Tragically, during the last decade or so of his life, Faraday sank into senility, a condition in which one's mental powers decline. Queen Victoria provided a house for the great scientist to live out his days. Faraday died in 1867. The *farad,* a unit used to measure electrical capacitance, was named for him.

Joseph Henry

Joseph Henry (1797-1878) was one of the greatest scientists in the United States during the 1800's. Much of his work in the field of electromagnetism paralleled that of Michael Faraday, of Great Britain. But in most cases, Faraday published first and received the credit. Joseph Henry was the first director of the Smithsonian Institution in Washington, D.C.

Like other scientists of his time, Joseph Henry was intrigued by Hans Oersted's discovery in 1820 that a current-carrying wire produces a magnetic field. Oersted's experiment had established, for the first time, a definite connection between electricity and magnetism.

Henry began working on electromagnets. He strengthened an electromagnet by winding many layers around the iron core. In 1831, developing a similar idea, Michael Faraday discovered electromagnetic induction, that is, generating electric current in a wire loop by the movement of a magnet. It is the principle

Joseph Henry publishes his discoveries on self-induction.

 1835

by which our electricity is generated today. Henry made the same discovery at about the same time, but Faraday made his findings public.

Faraday and Henry also discovered—at about the same time—that interrupting a current in a wire produces an opposite current in the same wire. Henry published a paper on this principle, called self-induction, in 1835. Although Faraday had again published first, Henry is today given credit for this discovery.

Henry developed an early electric motor, the first telegraph, and he invented the electrical relay. He also developed an early transformer.

Congress established the Smithsonian Institution in 1846 and invited Joseph Henry to be its first director. Henry accepted the offer. The Smithsonian Institution was chartered as an organization to promote scientific research and exploration and as a museum for the American people. Serving as the first director of a new institution, Henry provided skilled, strong leadership that helped assure the Smithsonian's success.

While at the Smithsonian, Henry took a great interest in meteorological research. *Meteorology* is the study of weather and climate. He encouraged the development of meteorology as a scientific discipline.

During the last decade of his life, Henry served as president of the National Academy of Sciences.

Joseph Henry was born in Albany, New York, in 1797. He received little formal education, but educated himself by reading constantly. Through his efforts and hard work, Joseph was able to gain admission to the Albany Academy. After graduating, he served as an instructor in science and mathematics at the academy. Henry began his experiments on electromagnetism while at Albany. In 1832 Henry joined the faculty of the College of New Jersey, now Princeton. He remained there until going to the Smithsonian in 1846. Joseph Henry died in 1878.

Joseph Henry has been honored by having an electromagnetic unit of measurement, the *henry,* named after him.

Sir Charles Lyell

Sir Charles Lyell (1797-1875) was a British geologist who is considered the founder of modern geology. Lyell published the most important geological textbook of the 1800's. His belief that changes in the earth's surface occur very slowly over long periods of time revolutionized the science of geology. His ideas also had a great impact on Charles Darwin, who eventually developed the modern theory of evolution according to natural selection.

Lyell rejected a popular geological theory known as "catastrophism." Supporters of this theory believed that the surface features of the earth—mountains, rivers, rock formations—resulted from violent, sudden upheavals occurring some time in the earth's recent past. But Lyell insisted that geological change takes place very, very slowly. It is occurring now as in the past, but is so slow that we humans are not aware of its action. A very important implication of Lyell's theory was that the earth must be very, very ancient. Before this time, most people had held the belief that the earth was only a few thousand years old. Furthermore, this belief had seemed consistent with Biblical accounts of earth history, so the church supported it as well.

Eventually, Lyell gathered proof for his theory in his studies of Mt. Etna, a volcano on the Italian island of Sicily. Lyell showed that Mt. Etna had been built up over a wide span of time by repeated eruptions.

Lyell gathered scientific data from many geological expeditions. He travelled in many parts of Europe and North America. This accumulated geological evidence enabled Lyell to write a three-volume textbook that became the standard in its field. Called *Principles of Geology,* Lyell's book went through many editions. Lyell and his wife, Mary Horner Lyell, spent much of their time working on revisions of this very popular textbook.

Principles of Geology had a tremendous impact on the scientific community. It is one of the books Charles Darwin carried when he accompanied the scientific expedition aboard H.M.S. *Beagle* in the 1830's. Lyell's emphasis on very slow and gradual change of features on the earth's surface strongly influenced Darwin's thinking. Later, Darwin's theory of evolution by natural selection—proposing slow, gradual changes in populations of organisms—would echo Lyell's ideas. In time,

Matthias Schleiden and **Theodor Schwann** propose that the cell is the basic structural and functional unit of all living things.

| **1830-1833** | **ca. 1838** | **ca. 1840** |

Charles Lyell publishes *Principles of Geology,* founding the modern science of geology.

Louis Agassiz theorizes that huge sheets of ice once extended from the North Pole to Central Europe, dramatically changing the earth's surface.

most scientists would come to accept Lyell's view of geological change.

In 1838 Lyell published *Elements of Geology.* In this book, Lyell described rocks and fossils of Europe. He identified relatively young fossils and very old ones.

Lyell was personally skeptical about Darwin's theory of natural selection when it was first published in 1859. But eventually, he came to accept Darwin's theory of evolution. Lyell supported Darwin's theory in a new edition of *Principles of Geology* published in 1865.

Lyell's contributions to geology went beyond theory. He firmly established many of the methods used by geologists ever since. His extensive geological expeditions provided models for future geological field work.

Charles Lyell was born of a well-to-do family at Kinnordy, Scotland, in 1797. His father was an amateur naturalist, and young Charles was educated at the best schools. He went to Oxford University at the age of 19 to study law. Though Lyell earned a degree (1819) and was licensed to practice law (1825), he devoted most of his life to geological research and expeditions, and writing. For a short period, in 1832-33, Lyell worked as a lecturer at King's College, London. But he gave up this work to have more time to devote to scientific work.

Lyell, a well-known figure in Victorian England, participated in many civic activities. He served on a team with the great physicist, Michael Faraday, to find ways to prevent mining disasters. He was also a commissioner for the Crystal Palace Exposition in 1851-52. (The Crystal Palace Exposition was a great fair of science and technology—rather like modern-day world's fairs—held in London.) Lyell also helped reform the curriculum (course of study) at Oxford University. Up to this time, training at the English universities—Oxford and Cambridge—had been dominated by the Church of England.

Lyell received many awards and honors. He was made a knight in 1848. He became personal friends with the British royal family. The Royal Society granted Lyell its highest award, the Copley Medal, in 1858.

Sir Charles Lyell died in 1875. He was buried in Westminster Abbey, a great honor for an English citizen. Many scientists, including Charles Darwin, acknowledged Lyell's enormous contributions to science.

The American astronomer **Maria Mitchell** *(below)* An 1889 drawing of **Maria Mitchell's** observatory *(right)* in Lynn, Massachusetts

Maria Mitchell

Maria Mitchell (1818-1889) was one of the first important astronomers in the United States. Mitchell made important studies of sunspots and satellites of planets. She gained international fame for her discovery of a new comet in 1847. The king of Denmark awarded her a gold medal for this achievement.

Mitchell was also the first woman member of the American Academy of Arts and Sciences. The academy admitted her in 1848.

Maria Mitchell was born in 1818 in Nantucket, Mass. As a young adult, she was librarian of the Nantucket Atheneum. Later she worked for the U.S. Nautical Almanac Office. From 1865 to 1888 Mitchell taught astronomy on the faculty of Vassar College. She served as director of the college's observatory and continued to make detailed astronomical observations.

Maria Mitchell died in 1889. She was elected to the Hall of Fame in 1905. The Nantucket Maria Mitchell Association supports a museum, scientific library, and observatory in her honor.

MARIA MITCHELL'S OBSERVATORY AT LYNN, MASS.

Crawford Long and **William T. G. Morton** discover that ether gas could safely be used to put patients to sleep during surgery.

ca. 1845

1846

Johann Galle and **Heinrich L. d'Arrest** discover the planet Neptune.

1847

Maria Mitchell, one of the first important astronomers in the U.S., discovers a new comet.

Hermann von Helmholtz

Hermann von Helmholtz (1821-1894) was a German scientist who made important contributions in several fields of science. He formulated one of the basic laws of physics, the law of conservation of energy. Helmholtz founded the modern science of acoustics (the study of sound) and contributed to our understanding of human hearing. He made important discoveries about the human nervous system. Helmholtz also contributed to the body of electrodynamic theory developed mainly by Michael Faraday and James Clerk Maxwell.

Helmholtz was one of the first scientists to discover and formulate the law of conservation of energy. This law states that energy can neither be created nor destroyed, only transformed from one form into another. This is also known as the first law of thermodynamics. It laid the foundation for an important area of physics that studies energy, heat, and work.

Helmholtz set out to discredit ways of thinking that he believed to be unscientific. During his youth, a theory called "vital force" enjoyed popularity. This theory claimed that a vital, or life, force guided many of the functions and processes in living organisms. For this reason, physical processes in organisms could not be analyzed according to the same scientific principles used in other fields. Helmholtz wanted to prove that such processes in living things are no different than those in the physical world. He insisted that biological processes could be analyzed experimentally and scientifically. In 1850 Helmholtz measured the speed of a nerve impulse. His conclusions proved that living matter and processes could be analyzed in the same ways as nonliving things. Helmholtz carried this idea further in his paper, "On the Conservation of Force." He stated that all forces (including those at work in living organisms) can be regarded as either matter or motion.

Helmholtz studied optics, the science of light and vision. In the course of this research, he invented the *ophthalmoscope.* This instrument is used by doctors to examine the eye.

Helmholtz conducted extensive research in the physics of sound. He laid the groundwork for the modern science of acoustics. He concentrated on two distinct areas of study: the physical properties of sound (sound waves) and the process of human hearing. Helmholtz correctly identified many structures in the ear that contribute to hearing. He published a scientific work on sound and hearing in 1863. Called *On the System of Tone,* this book established basic principles for the science of acoustics.

Helmholtz closely followed the work of British physicists Michael Faraday and James Maxwell Clerk in the area of electromagnetism. Helmholtz made important contributions to the mathematics of electromagnetism. Also, Helmholtz reasoned that electricity is made up of tiny particles. He thus suggested the existence of the electron, which was discovered by J.J. Thomson in 1897.

Hermann Helmholtz was born in Potsdam (near Berlin) in 1821. His father was a teacher of languages at an excellent *gymnasium*—a German high school. Young Hermann received a thorough education at his father's school.

Helmholtz attended medical school at the Friedrich Wilhelm Institute in Berlin on a scholarship. The condition of this scholarship was that he serve as an army doctor upon graduating. Later, Helmholtz held a number of teaching positions at German universities. Eventually, he settled at the University of Berlin, where he became professor of physics. In 1888 Helmholtz became the first director of the Physico-Technical Institute in Berlin. In 1882 Helmholtz was made a member of the German nobility in recognition of his scientific achievements. (In German, the name *von* preceded a nobleman's last name.) Helmholtz died in 1894.

Lord Kelvin

Lord Kelvin (1824-1907) was a great British physicist and inventor. Kelvin made important contributions to the area of physics known as thermodynamics. Kelvin made about 70 inventions for which he received patents. (A patent is a legal right of ownership of an invention.) He served as chief engineer for the laying of the transatlantic cable in the 1850's and 1860's.

Perhaps Kelvin's most important theoretical contribution to science is his formulation of the second law of thermodynamics. *Thermodynamics* studies various forms of energy, such as heat and work, and the conversion of

Late Nineteenth Century——1850-1899

1850

Hermann Helmholtz measures the speed of a human nerve impulse, proving that living matter could be analyzed in the same way as nonliving matter.

ca. 1850

James P. Joule discovers that energy and heat are interchangeable at a fixed rate.

energy forms. In the first law of thermodynamics, Hermann von Helmholtz and others had stated that energy can neither be created nor destroyed, but merely transformed. In the second law, Kelvin noted that not all forms of energy are equally interchangeable and that forms other than heat tend to change into heat. The law implied that a perfectly efficient machine cannot exist, for some energy will always leak out in the form of heat. Kelvin published these ideas in a scientific paper entitled, "On the Dynamical Theory of Heat."

Kelvin proposed a temperature scale that includes absolute zero as its lower limit. This is now called the Kelvin scale. Absolute zero is the theoretical temperature at which the motion of all atoms and molecules stops. Absolute zero has never been reached in experiments, and many scientists think it is impossible.

Kelvin became a consultant to the company that was laying the first transatlantic telegraph cable in the 1850's. Eventually, Kelvin was hired by the company to direct the cable work. Kelvin patented several inventions for use with the cable, including a telegraphic receiver. He became wealthy from this project and received many honors.

Out of Kelvin's interest in sailing came a number of other useful inventions. These included a compass (used by the British navy), a machine to calculate tides, and sounding equipment.

In all, Kelvin patented 70 inventions. He published over 600 scientific papers.

Kelvin worked with P.G. Tait, another British physicist, to write a textbook on physics. Entitled *Treatise on Natural Philosophy* and first published in 1867, this work became a basic textbook for students of physics.

Lord Kelvin was born William Thomson in Belfast, Ireland, in 1824. (He was made a member of nobility later in life, at which time he became Lord Kelvin.) Thomson's father, a mathematics teacher, stimulated the boy's interest in mathematics. William's family moved to Glasgow, Scotland, and the boy entered the university at the age of 10. By the time he was 17, William had published several scientific articles.

Later, William studied at Cambridge University and graduated with high honors. He was appointed a professor at Glasgow University at the age of 22. There he remained for his entire career. Thomson was elected to the

Royal Society in 1851 and served as its president in later life.

Thomson's many inventions and especially his work on the transatlantic cable won him many awards and honors. Queen Victoria made him a knight in 1866. In 1892, Thomson was made Baron Kelvin of Largs. At his death in 1907, Kelvin was buried in Westminster Abbey, one of the greatest honors that can come to an English citizen.

Rudolf Virchow

Rudolf Virchow (1821-1902), a German medical scientist, anthropologist, and politician, is considered the father of modern pathology. *Pathology* is the study of diseases and their effects on body tissues and organs. Virchow also helped firmly establish the cellular theory of organisms, the theory that all plants and animals are made up of cells. As a politician, Virchow also contributed to public health in Germany and elsewhere.

As a young man, Virchow became convinced that the body tissues of organisms, plants, and animals are composed of cells. Virchow was strongly influenced by a handful of scientists who promoted the cell theory. A basic principle formulated by this group was that every cell descends from another cell. Another principle was that most of the basic physical functions in organisms, such as respiration, actually take place at the level of cells. Virchow extended this idea to the study of pathology. He claimed that one must study disease at the cellular level in order to understand the changes that occur in diseased tissue.

Virchow published his ideas on pathology in 1858 in a highly important textbook called *Cellular Pathology.* In this work, Virchow completely dismissed traditional theories of pathology. He insisted that diseases must be studied at the level of cells. In time, Virchow's ideas radically changed medicine and the study of biology.

Virchow studied and wrote about the effects of many diseases on body tissue. In 1845, while still a medical intern, he described leukemia, which he called "white blood." Virchow's paper on the topic became a medical

Rudolf Virchow, German pathologist, as shown in an 1887 engraving

Lord Kelvin publishes "On the Dynamical Theory of Heat," which contains the second law of thermodynamics.

Sir William Perkin creates the first synthetic dye.

1851   ca. 1855   1856

Robert Bunsen and **Gustav Kirchhoff** discover that atoms of each chemical element produce a certain set of spectral lines; this leads to the identification of the elements that make up a star.

classic. Virchow also described the diseased cells in many malignant (cancerous) tumors, including sarcoma and melanoma.

Virchow studied certain diseases of the circulatory system. He described *thrombosis,* the formation of a blood clot, and *embolus,* a closely related condition. An embolus is a clot that breaks free and travels in the bloodstream to other sites, often damaging body tissues.

Virchow also described the process of inflammation. In inflammation, tissues around a wound undergo changes as the body's immune system (including white blood cells) fights infection.

Virchow determined the life cycle of *trichina,* a dangerous animal parasite that enters the human body through eating infected meat. His studies clarified the process of trichina development and infection. Because of these studies, Virchow became a strong advocate of government meat inspection. Due to the efforts of people such as Virchow, most countries in the West and many elsewhere have strict government guidelines for growing livestock and packaging meat. Trichinosis, infection by trichina, is now a rare disease in these parts of the world. Virchow fought for many other public health issues, including proper sewage disposal and adequate hospital facilities.

The modern method of performing autopsies (physical examination of dead bodies) can be attributed to Virchow. Virchow pioneered a more thorough approach in autopsies, by which considerable information about the means of death and the person's general condition of health prior to death can be revealed. These techniques are important in murder investigations, for instance.

Virchow influenced future generations of medical researchers through his writings and through his students. One of his most famous medical students was William Osler, the Canadian physician who discovered blood platelets.

Co-founder of *Archives for Pathological Anatomy and Physiology,* Virchow edited this medical journal for many years. It is still being published today. In 1848-1849, Virchow published a weekly paper, *Medical Reform,* in which he proposed changes in the German medical profession.

In the 1860's, Virchow became extremely interested in archaeology (the study of objects left by previous civilizations). He discovered and excavated (dug out) some ancient dwellings and forts in northern Germany. In 1869 Virchow help found two German archaeological societies. He served as chief editor for a journal of archaeology and anthropology (the study of development of human cultures) for many years. Virchow accompanied archaeologist Heinrich Schliemann on archaeological digs at Troy and in Egypt. Schliemann was famous for discovering the site of ancient Troy.

Rudolf Virchow was born in Pomerania in 1821. (Pomerania is a coastal region on the Baltic Sea now shared by Poland and East Germany.) He attended the Friedrich Wilhelm Institute in Berlin and graduated with a degree in medicine in 1843. He worked in his early years at Charité Hospital, a major hospital in Berlin. In 1848 a political revolution broke out in Berlin and elsewhere in Europe. Virchow, a liberal thinker, became involved in revolutionary action.

In 1849 Virchow accepted a post as professor of pathological anatomy at the University of Würzburg, a city in south central Germany. There he trained many medical students. In 1856 Virchow became a professor at the University of Berlin. From that time until his death, Virchow lived in Berlin.

Virchow became a politician and served at many levels of government. These included the Berlin City Council, the Prussian state legislature, and the parliament for the German Empire in the 1880's and 1890's. Virchow promoted progressive policies and sponsored many reforms in public health. In 1873 Virchow was elected to the Prussian Academy of Sciences. He died in 1902.

Charles Darwin

Charles Darwin (1809-1882), a British naturalist, was one of the most important and controversial scientists of modern times. Darwin is most known for his theory of evolution by natural selection. This theory, although never proved, has been widely accepted by biologists since Darwin's lifetime.

Darwin's theory of natural selection may be summarized as follows. All species of living organisms have evolved, or gradually changed, from simpler organisms over vast

Rudolf Virchow publishes *Cellular Pathology,* establishing the idea that diseases should be studied at the cellular level.

1858

Charles Darwin, the English naturalist, as painted by
John Collier, T. H. Huxley's
son-in-law

periods of time. Human beings, like all other plants and animals, have evolved from simpler organisms. The process by which evolution happens is known as *natural selection.*

To understand the theory of natural selection, imagine a population of birds of the same species. Now and then, a bird with a mutation (a genetic change) is born into the bird population. The mutation may be helpful to the individual bird. If a bird is born with a longer, sharper beak, for example, it might be able to get food more easily than its bird relatives. In such a case, the bird with the long beak might mate with another bird, passing its long beak to its offspring. These long-beaked birds would, in turn, have an advantage in getting

food. Eventually, over time, the long-beaked birds might overtake birds with shorter beaks in the total population. The reason is simply that the long-beaked birds are more successful at getting food, and therefore, surviving. According to the theory, natural selection can also work in the opposite way. An individual with a harmful mutation—a bird with a very short, dull beak, for example—would be less likely to survive and produce offspring. Birds in the population who possess this type of beak would probably eventually die out.

Darwin developed these ideas and his habits of scientific observations while on a long scientific journey aboard H.M.S. *Beagle,* a survey ship, in the early 1830's. In South America he found fossils of extinct animals that resembled living animals. Most important were Darwin's observations of plant and animal life in the Galapagos Islands in the Pacific Ocean off the western coast of South America. Many plant and animal species with small variations among populations inhabited these islands. These observations helped Darwin develop his theory of natural selection.

In addition to his ideas about biology and evolution, Darwin developed some important ideas about geology, the study of the earth, while on this voyage. Darwin had brought a copy of Charles Lyell's textbook, *Principles of Geology,* aboard ship. Lyell believed that changes in the earth's surface occur very slowly, over vast periods of time. In contrast, many influential scientists of the time believed that such changes occur violently in short spans of time. Darwin was converted to Lyell's way of thinking by his own observations of geologic formations in South America. Furthermore, he formulated an original theory on the formation of coral reefs. This theory was eventually accepted by geologists.

Charles Darwin returned to England from his extensive travels in 1836. He was well received by the scientific community there. Within several years, he was elected to the Geological Society, the Atheneum—an exclusive club for men who were prominent in literature, art, or science—and the Royal Society. He also developed friendships with influential scientists. Darwin worked on several publishing projects related to his travels aboard the *Beagle* in these years. His early books include a journal of his research aboard the *Beagle* and *The Structure and Distribution of Coral Reefs.*

Charles Darwin publishes
The Origin of Species,
introducing the theory of
evolution.

 1859

In the meantime, Darwin was refining his theory of natural selection. But he delayed publishing it for many years. Darwin may have feared the controversy he expected to erupt. He enjoyed a comfortable and, in many ways, conventional life, which he did not wish to endanger.

Finally, Darwin's scientist friends persuaded him to present a paper on natural selection to the Linnean Society of London in 1858. In the following year, 1859, Darwin published his theories in *The Origins of Species by Means of Natural Selection.* The book proved immensely popular—and controversial—for decades. Many scientists accepted Darwin's theory of natural selection. But many other people, especially religious leaders, were shocked by it. To them, Darwin's theory seemed to suggest that living things had developed naturally on earth without action by God. The first major public debate on the subject occurred in June, 1860, at a meeting of the British Association for the Advancement of Science. Darwin's friends and fellow scientists, T.H. Huxley and Joseph Hooker, debated the Anglican bishop of Oxford, Samuel Wilberforce. Bishop Wilberforce raised the question of human descent from apes—a logical conclusion drawn from *On the Origin of Species.* Though Huxley and Hooker held their ground against Wilberforce, the question has remained controversial to this day.

In fact, Darwin confronted this issue directly in his book, *The Descent of Man, and Selection in Relation to Sex,* published in 1871. In this book, Darwin made clear that he believed that humans had descended from the apes. In another book, *The Expression of the Emotions in Man and Animals* (1872), Darwin attempted to show that emotions such as love, hatred, and anger exist among animals as well as in humans. These theories seemed to draw humans and the rest of the animal world even closer together. They proved important to later scientific development in fields such as animal behavior and communications theory.

Darwin seemed to become more interested in plants and ecology during his later years. In his final book, *The Formation of Vegetable Mould, Through the Action of Worms* (1881), Darwin showed how worms help clean the environment by eating dead leaves and producing waste matter that renews the soil. It proved an important early contribution to the science of ecology.

Darwin was born into a comfortable family life in the English upper middle class. His father and grandfather had both been successful medical doctors. Darwin's father sent him to Cambridge University in 1827 to study divinity, in preparation for a career in the Church of England. But Darwin seemed to have little interest in his studies or his chosen career.

During the Cambridge years, however, Darwin developed a close friendship with the botanist, John Stevens Henslow. This association sparked Darwin's excitement in science. With Henslow's recommendation, Darwin was able to gain a position as ship naturalist with the *Beagle* expedition in 1831. This experience, of course, changed Darwin's life and led to his scientific accomplishments.

In 1839 Darwin married. Financially secure, Darwin and his wife, Emma, spent most of their years in semi-retirement in a village outside of London. They had 10 children. Although not required to work for a living, Darwin remained active in scientific circles through his life. He kept in touch with his scientist friends and attended many scientific meetings and conventions.

Charles Darwin died in 1882. In death, he was granted the great honor of burial at Westminster Abbey in London.

Louis Pasteur

Louis Pasteur (1822-1895) was a great French chemist and microbiologist. The term *pasteurization,* used most often to name the process by which fresh milk is protected from rapid spoilage, comes from his name. Pasteur made extremely important contributions to biology, medicine, chemistry, and industry.

Most of Pasteur's scientific work concerned the effects of microbes, tiny organisms that can be seen only with a microscope. In Pasteur's time, many natural processes caused by microbes were not understood. He studied fermentation, the chemical process by which grape juice can be changed into wine, for instance. Pasteur found that living organisms—microbes—cause fermentation.

This was an extremely important discovery, both for theoretical science and for the wine industry. Pasteur realized that the growth of

Louis Pasteur develops the process known as pasteurization.

 ca. 1863-1864

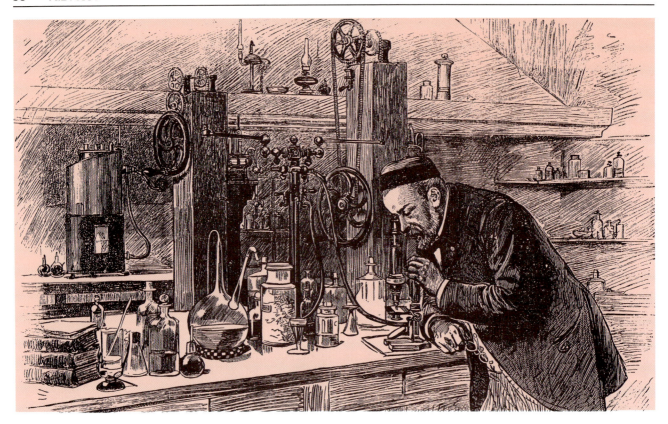

Louis Pasteur, the French chemist, is shown in his laboratory in a 19th century engraving

the beneficial microbes could be controlled before and during fermentation. When wine matured, the microbes—harmful as well as helpful—could be killed by heat. (This is the process of pasteurization applied to wine.) These procedures made winemaking far more scientific and profitable. Pasteur had saved the wine industry millions of francs. Pasteur applied the same ideas to the beer and milk industries—with similar success.

Meanwhile, Pasteur became deeply involved in a related scientific problem of a more theoretical nature. Many scientists of the time believed that the observed effects of microbes, such as fermentation and spoilage of food, occur because the organisms "spontaneously generate" in substances. By this they meant that microbes form out of nonliving matter by means other than reproduction. Others rejected this idea. In any event, a controversy was raging over the theory of spontaneous generation at the time that Pasteur became involved.

Pasteur approached the problem scientifically and experimentally. He devised a set of ingenious experiments that isolated test substances (such as unfermented liquid) from all but pure, filtrated air. He proved that food and other organic matter does not spontaneously generate microbes. Rather, microbes enter substances from the air (or from other contaminated objects). Such organisms exist naturally in the air and most other substances in nature. They are already in grape juice, for instance, when it is bottled and aged for fermentation in a wine cellar. Thus, Pasteur settled once and for all the spontaneous generation controversy.

At the request of the French government, Pasteur applied his knowledge of microbes to a serious problem in the French silk industry. A devastating disease was killing off silkworms, which produced the silk fibers that are woven into cloth. Unless something could be done soon, the silk industry would be ruined.

Pasteur moved to the south of France so that he could work closely with the silk producers. Within a few years, he had discovered the germs that cause several varieties of the silkworm disease. This knowledge enabled the silk producers to test their stock of silkworms and to remove diseased worms from healthy ones. Using the methods developed by Pasteur, the silk industry survived and recovered. Pasteur had performed yet another great service for industry. Beyond this, Pasteur had established the practice of carrying scientific research "into the field." His methods, oriented toward identifying a problem and then finding a solution, would provide a model for future researchers.

Pasteur continued his studies of microbes and disease, despite suffering a serious stroke at the height of his career in 1868. He developed vaccinations to protect sheep from anthrax and poultry from chicken cholera. These diseases had ravaged farm livestock. The scientific basis for this work was the theory of vaccination. To produce a vaccination, the researcher takes a disease-causing microbe and kills or weakens it. When the weakened germ is introduced into a human or animal body, it causes the body to develop immunity, or resistance, to the germ in its strong, healthy form. Edward Jenner had used similar ideas in developing a smallpox vaccine in 1796.

Pasteur turned his attention to a terrible disease that attacks both humans and animals. That disease, rabies, is transmitted to humans by infected animals—dogs, cats, squirrels, or other animals—through a bite wound. Pasteur devoted intensive research to the problem of rabies. He came to the conclusion that a virus, unable to be seen with a regular microscope, causes rabies. Despite the difficulties of working with a virus, Pasteur managed to produce a weakened form of the virus, which he believed might serve as a vaccine. Before he could test the substance thoroughly, however, a neighboring child was bitten by a rabid dog. The parents, frantic to save their son, persuaded Pasteur to use the rabies vaccine. This he did. The boy survived without ill effects.

Pasteur's outstanding achievement in developing a rabies vaccine earned him praise and further fame. In 1888 a laboratory dedicated to rabies research was opened in Paris and named for him. Louis Pasteur accepted the directorship of the Pasteur Institute and remained there until his death in 1895.

Pasteur also made contributions to other areas of science. He did pioneering work in stereochemistry, the study of the ways in which different crystalline structures can cause chemically identical substances to have different properties. Pasteur discovered this effect in two apparently identical acids that had very different outward characteristics. From these observations, he developed a theory of molecular asymmetry. Pasteur's theory laid the groundwork for the field of stereochemistry.

Louis Pasteur was born in 1822 in eastern France of a long line of tanners. (A tanner is a worker who tans, or processes, animal hides into leather.) As a boy, Louis seemed interested only in painting and drawing. But later he developed an interest in science. Pasteur attended several colleges, earning degrees up to a Ph.D. in 1847. At age 26 he presented a paper on stereochemistry to the Paris Academy of Sciences.

Pasteur served on the faculties of several colleges and universities as a young adult. In 1849 he married. In 1854 Pasteur was appointed a dean of science at the University of Lille. Lille is an industrial city in northeastern France. While serving in this position, Pasteur developed new programs, such as night classes, to extend educational opportunities to industrial workers.

Pasteur continued teaching on the faculties of several French colleges and universities until the French emperor, Napoleon III, provided a laboratory for him in 1867. After this time, Pasteur was able to devote most of his efforts to research. In the meantime, Pasteur had been elected to the French Academy of Sciences in 1862.

In 1873 Pasteur was elected to the Academy of Medicine and in 1882, to the Académie Française. The French Parliament made an award of money to Pasteur in 1874 so that he could carry on his research without financial worries. His greatest honor was the establishment of the Pasteur Institute in 1888. This great medical research facility is still conducting research on diseases—such as AIDS—today.

Pasteur was active in the scientific discussions and controversies of his day. He communicated with other scientists and became friends with some, notably the British surgeon, Joseph Lister. Although Pasteur could sometimes be argumentative and harsh, he was widely recognized as one of the greatest scientists of his time. His reputation has not dimmed with the passing of almost a century.

James Clerk Maxwell

James Clerk Maxwell (1831-1879) was one of the greatest physicists in history. Like another great British physicist, Sir Isaac Newton, he investigated many different areas of physical science. Also like Newton, he contributed theories that opened new avenues of thought and scientific development.

Maxwell's work on electricity, magnetism, and force fields was his greatest achievement. In this area of research, he built on theories that Michael Faraday had developed. Maxwell and Faraday exchanged ideas on this subject. (Faraday died in 1867.)

Faraday studied the electromagnetic force field produced by electrical current. He became convinced that the forces at work in such a field are not confined to the conductor. The conductor is, rather, simply a medium through which the force is exerted. The logical conclusion of this idea is that lines of force extend into the space that surrounds a conductor. Faraday's idea was an original and important one. But he was not able to work it out completely.

Maxwell took Faraday's idea and developed it into a complete *electromagnetic theory.* This theory explains how electrical current radiates energy—such as radio waves and microwaves—into space. Eventually the electromagnetic theory was applied to the physical properties of radioactive materials and the energy they produce and to other types of energy as well.

Maxwell then applied principles of electromagnetic theory to light. He discovered that light behaves in the same way as electromagnetic forces and concluded that light is a type of electromagnetic force.

Several years later, in the 1880's, the German physicist Heinrich Hertz produced radio waves in a laboratory setting. Hertz's experiments completely confirmed Maxwell's electromagnetic theory.

The importance of Maxwell's electromagnetic theory can hardly be overestimated. For the most part, twentieth century technology would have been impossible without it. Inventions such as television, radio, radar, satellite communications, and many others are a result of electromagnetic theory. In fact, communications as we know them would be unthinkable without Maxwell's pioneering work. And without the long-distance communications made possible by electromagnetic waves, there would be no space exploration.

Furthermore, Maxwell's work laid the theoretical foundations for an avalanche of scientific developments to come. Development of the quantum theory—probably the most important scientific theory of our century—is partly an outgrowth of Maxwell's study of light and other electromagnetic energy. His development of field theory—the study of force fields created by magnetism, electricity, or other natural forces—also strongly influenced later physicists. Albert Einstein, for example, spent much of his later life trying to formulate a unified field theory that would explain all forces in the universe in unified, mathematical terms. This work, which continues today, would have been impossible without Maxwell's basic theories.

Maxwell made important contributions to other areas of science. He developed a kinetic theory of gases that helped clarify the nature of gases. In this theory, Maxwell explained the behavior of a gas in terms of the movement of its molecules. He calculated mathematically the movements of the molecules and showed how these individual movements, multiplied billions of times, explained many properties of gases. This work enabled chemists to determine mathematically—and to predict—the characteristics of a gas.

Maxwell developed a theory of color vision and made one of the first color photographs. He also studied the rings of the planet Saturn.

Maxwell studied the work of contemporary and previous scientists and learned from them. He was particularly interested in the work of Henry Cavendish, a great English scientist of the 1700's who had been largely ignored in his own time. Maxwell drew on Cavendish's work with electricity in formulating his own theories. Maxwell also tried to draw public attention to the scientific achievements of Cavendish, who had died in 1810. He published in 1879 some of the scientific papers by Cavendish on electricity.

In the early 1870's, descendants of Henry Cavendish endowed a scientific laboratory at Cambridge University. James Clerk Maxwell accepted the invitation to become the first Cavendish professor of physics. He designed the laboratory and recruited its staff. Maxwell's work was so successful that by the early 1900's, the Cavendish Laboratory became perhaps the most important center for physics re-

James Clerk Maxwell predicts the existence of electromagnetic waves.

1864

search in the world.

James Clerk Maxwell was born in Edinburgh, Scotland, in 1831. James's mother died when he was quite young. The boy developed a very close lifelong relationship with his father. The older Maxwell valued education and had personal connections with the scientific community in Edinburgh. James went to school at the Edinburgh Academy. Edinburgh's Royal Society published several scientific papers of the brilliant, 19-year-old James.

Maxwell went to Cambridge University, eventually winning a mathematical fellowship and graduating with high honors. In 1856 he gained an appointment to the faculty of Marischal College in Aberdeen, Scotland, near his family home. (His father, however, died in that year.) During this period, Maxwell married. In 1860 he joined the faculty of King's College in London. There Maxwell stayed for five years, after which he retired to his family home in Scotland to devote his time to research. Retirement ended for him in 1871 when the unexpected invitation to establish the Cavendish Laboratory came. Maxwell died, a relatively young man in his forties, in 1879.

Maxwell's published scientific writings include *Theory of Heat* and *Treatise on Electricity and Magnetism.*

Sir Joseph Lister

Sir Joseph Lister (1827-1912) founded antiseptic (germ-free) surgery. Before this advance, most surgical operations resulted in infection, and about half of the surgical patients died. Even an operation we would consider minor could be life-threatening.

Before the later 1800's, medical science had little understanding of germs and how they cause disease. Joseph Lister, a professor of medicine and surgeon in Glasgow, Scotland, began to study the problem of postoperative infection. He noted that even in the newest, finest medical facilities, the death rate from infection after surgery ran at about 50 per cent. Lister developed a theory that airborne dust carries a substance that causes sepsis, that is, infection. Lister concluded that the sepsis could be prevented only if a barrier could be put between the surgical wound and the air.

This he did by using carbolic acid sprays to kill germs in the air.

In surgical tests conducted during the period 1865-1869, Lister dramatically showed the effectiveness of the new approach. The postoperative mortality rate (the percentage of patients who died) dropped to 15 per cent, whereas a near-50 per cent rate had been normal before.

Before he began the new surgical procedures, Lister learned of the work of Louis Pasteur in France. Pasteur identified a number of germs and proved that microbes (tiny organisms) cause a wide range of effects, from fermentation in wine to spoilage of food. Lister then realized that microbes cause infection in surgical patients. A surgical cut, if untreated, admits germs into the body. Once inside the body, the germs are very difficult to control.

Many doctors in Europe and the United States questioned or opposed Lister's surgical techniques. Lister took advantage of an opportunity in 1877 to put all opposition to rest. In a London hospital, he performed a very delicate operation that had in the past almost always resulted in infection. The operation involved wiring a fractured kneecap. The controversial operation generated wide publicity and much criticism. Lister, however, was confident. He operated under antiseptic conditions, and the patient recovered completely. From this time on, Lister's surgical techniques were adopted far and wide.

Today's germ-free surgical environments are the result of Lister's ideas. In time, surgeons understood that germs can enter the body from almost any point of contact, not just from the air. For this reason, surgeons scrub and put on surgical gowns, masks, and gloves before an operation.

Joseph Lister was born in 1827, the son of Quaker parents. His father, an amateur scientist, was made a member of the Royal Society of London. Joseph had a thorough education in Quaker schools. He attended the University College, London, graduating with a bachelor of medicine degree in 1852. In 1853 he was appointed assistant to James Syme, a great surgical teacher in Edinburgh, Scotland. In 1856 Lister was appointed surgeon to the Edinburgh Royal Infirmary. In 1861 he went to Glasgow, Scotland, to teach on the faculty of Glasgow University and to serve as surgeon to the Glasgow Royal Infirmary. This is the hospital at which Lister pioneered his antiseptic surgical

Joseph Lister pioneers antiseptic surgery.

 1865

Friedrich Kekulé von Stradonitz describes the molecular structure of benzene, laying the foundations for modern organic chemistry.

techniques. Later, Lister returned to Edinburgh and then went to King's College in London (1877).

Lister became famous during his lifetime. He became popular with the French and the Germans, because his surgical techniques saved many lives during the Franco-Prussian War of 1870-1871. Lister made trips to Germany and the United States to tour the surgical facilities in those countries. In recognition of his great achievement, the British government made Lister a baron, a member of the British nobility.

Lister lived into old age. He became blind and deaf before his death in 1912.

Friedrich August Kekulé von Stradonitz

Friedrich August Kekulé von Stradonitz (1829-1896) was a German chemist who laid the foundations of modern organic chemistry. Organic chemistry is the field of research and industry that is concerned with chemical compounds based on carbon. Because of its particular atomic structure, carbon is able to form a tremendous number and variety of compounds. Carbon atoms can link with other carbon atoms as well as with atoms of other elements. Carbon often bonds with hydrogen, oxygen, nitrogen, or various combinations of these elements. All life as we know it is based on organic chemistry. Also, all the fossil fuels that we use are organic compounds. So are many medicines, including penicillin, for instance. Today, chemical research laboratories constantly synthesize, that is, make, new organic compounds. These are used for many purposes, from plastics to insect-killing substances.

Kekulé discovered several important principles of organic chemistry. First, he realized that the carbon atom is *tetravalent;* that is, it has four valences. A valence is the ability of one electron of an atom to combine with free electrons of other atoms. Thus, carbon has four such free electrons. Kekulé also understood that the four valences in a carbon atom are spread evenly apart. As a result, the structure of the carbon atom can be imagined as a tetrahedron (a pyramid with equal sides). This

idea is helpful when examining the structure of organic compounds.

From these insights, Kekulé concluded that carbon and other elements bond together to form long chains of molecules. Kekulé then applied his new understanding to the study of benzene, an organic substance. Kekulé tried to determine the chemical structure of benzene. He grappled with this problem with little success. Then one night in a dream, he saw the benzene molecule as a snake chasing its tail in a circle. When he woke up, Kekulé knew he had the solution for benzene's molecular structure: it is shaped like a ring. This story has often been quoted as a striking example of the subconscious (dreaming) mind helping the conscious (waking) mind solve a problem. Kekulé's solution of benzene structure opened new avenues of study and research in organic chemistry.

In addition to his work with benzene, Kekulé conducted important research on a variety of organic compounds. He also wrote an important four-volume textbook on organic chemistry.

Friedrich August Kekulé was born in Darmstadt, a city in southwestern Germany, in 1829. In later life he was granted a title of nobility. He added the words "von Stradonitz" to his name at that time.

As a young student, Kekulé intended to become an architect. He changed his mind in favor of chemistry, however, while attending the University of Giessen in Germany. He earned a doctorate and went to Paris to study with the chemist, Charles Frédéric Gerhardt. Gerhardt's ideas about organic compounds strongly influenced Kekulé. Later, Kekulé taught at universities in Heidelberg, Germany, and Ghent, Belgium. He moved to Bonn, Germany, in 1865.

Gregor Johann Mendel

Gregor Johann Mendel (1822-1884) discovered the basic laws of heredity, the process by which particular traits are passed from one generation of an organism to the next. His work established the foundations of genetics. Genetics is the science that studies the process of heredity at the level of the living cell

Gregor Mendel publishes his pioneering work in heredity.

1866

and its parts. Although Mendel's work was not recognized during his lifetime, he is now regarded as one of the greatest scientists of the 1800's.

Mendel lived most of his life as a monk in a Roman Catholic monastery. He developed an interest in science and particularly in horticulture, the growing of plants. Mendel used the monastery's garden to grow pea plants. These plants provided the data Mendel needed to formulate his theories on heredity.

Mendel knew that many plants and animals reproduce sexually. That is, a male and a female each produces a special sex cell, called a *gamete*. A male gamete and female gamete unite to form the beginning of a new organism. But Mendel wanted to learn more about the process by which traits from each of the parents are passed on to the new generation.

Mendel set up experiments to study the process of heredity. He identified several traits of pea plants that would be easy to identify in each generation. For example, he noticed that some peas had smooth skin, while others had wrinkled skin. Mendel crossed a plant having one trait (such as the smooth pea) with a plant having another (the wrinkled pea). He produced several generations of offspring, observing the pattern of traits (the pea skin-type) in each generation. From careful observation of a large amount of data, Mendel was able to understand the basic principles of heredity.

Mendel believed that each gamete contained units of heredity that pass on traits. (We now call these units *genes*.) When the male and female gametes join together, the new organism contains two pairs of genes—one from each parent—for each trait. Some genes are *dominant*. Others are *recessive*. In a gene pair, a dominant gene expresses its trait and cancels out the effect of the recessive gene (though it is still present in the cell).

Mendel went on to formulate some basic scientific laws that govern heredity. Mendel's first law is called the *Law of Segregation*. It states that gene pairs segregate (separate) randomly—that is, without any definite pattern—when a gamete is formed in the parent organism. Each gamete contains half the set of genes in a regular parent cell. If a gamete joins with another gamete to form a new organism, the original number of genes is restored. (In other words, each gamete contributes one-half of the total number of genes.) The focus of the Law of Segregation is, then,

on the forming of a gamete. Mendel proved this law through data collected from his experiments.

Mendel's second law is called the *Law of Independent Assortment*. It states that each trait is passed on independently of all other traits. This law suggested that every gene pair operates as an independent unit. Again, Mendel's experimental results seemed to prove this conclusion. Later research, however, showed that genes are linked together on chromosomes. Still, Mendel's second law holds true in many cases.

Mendel announced his theories on heredity in 1865 and had them published in a scientific journal in 1866. The journal was circulated throughout Europe and America. Scientists largely ignored Mendel's work. Then in 1900—after Mendel's death—three European scientists doing research on heredity came across Mendel's original scientific article. The scientists, Carl Erich Correns, Erich Tschermak von Seysenegg, and Hugo de Vries, realized that Mendel had discovered the basic principles of heredity 35 years earlier. They made Mendel's work known throughout the scientific community.

The importance of Mendel's discoveries can hardly be overestimated. A great deal of the modern science of biology is based on an understanding of the basic principles of heredity. Mendel's theories also help explain how Darwin's theory of evolution by natural selection works. (Although never proven, Darwin's theory is accepted by many scientists.) Without a basic understanding of heredity, the science of genetics would not exist. Today, genetics is one of the most active fields of science. It holds promises of new medical treatments for many diseases—as well as challenges and complex ethical problems.

Johann Mendel was born in Austrian Silesia (now a part of Czechoslovakia) in 1822. In 1843 he joined a Roman Catholic monastery at Brünn, Moravia (now Brno, Czechoslovakia) and took the monastic name of Gregor. Using the monastery library, Gregor taught himself the basics of science. In 1851-53 the monastery sent him to the University of Vienna to study science.

During the 1850's and 1860's, Mendel taught in a technical high school at Brünn. Ironically, he never passed the test for teacher's certification. The first time he took this exam, he scored especially poorly in biology. It is dur-

A 1862 photograph of **Gregor Johann Mendel,** the Austrian monk and botanist

 1868

Julius von Sachs publishes a landmark textbook on botany; he founds the modern science of plant physiology.

ing this period that Mendel conducted most of his experiments on plant heredity. In 1868 Mendel was elected abbot (leader) of the monastery. From this time on, most of his time was taken with administrative duties. Gregor Mendel died in 1884, unrecognized as the great scientist he really was.

Dmitri Ivanovich Mendeleev

Dmitri Ivanovich Mendeleev (1834-1907) was a Russian chemist who formulated a periodic law to describe the relationships among all the chemical elements. The *periodic law* states that the properties of chemical elements occur in repeating patterns. Mendeleev demonstrated this law by organizing the known elements in a periodic table according to their atomic weights. The grouping showed that elements within a vertical column have similar properties.

Mendeleev found gaps in his periodic table. He realized that certain elements had not yet been discovered. Judging from the relationships of the elements in his periodic table, Mendeleev predicted the properties of three missing elements.

At first, many scientists rejected Mendeleev's periodic law. Within 20 years, however, the 3 elements predicted by Mendeleev had been discovered. Moreover, they possessed the properties Mendeleev had predicted. These discoveries proved the correctness of Mendeleev's periodic law.

In the early 1900's, the periodic law would prove critical in work with radioactive elements. Radioactive elements decay, or break down, into other elements. Physicists studying the products of radioactive decay use the periodic law to identify them.

For a time, Mendeleev worked as a science writer and editor as well as a professor. In 1868-1870 he wrote his own textbook on chemistry for use with his classes. Entitled *Principles of Chemistry,* it became a classic textbook in its field.

Like another scientist of his time, Louis Pasteur, Mendeleev applied his scientific knowledge to industry and agriculture. For a time, he ran a small farm according to scientific principles. He demonstrated that crop yields could be greatly improved by scientific methods. At this time, Russia was a largely agricultural—and poor—country. Any improvement in agriculture was very important to the nation's economy and to the health of its people.

Mendeleev made several important contributions to industry. He brought back ideas from the French chemical industry after attending the Paris Exhibition (fair) in 1867. He applied French methods to the Russian soda industry. He also worked to improve the Russian petroleum industry. Russia was just beginning to develop modern industry at this time. Mendeleev's contributions would prove important as Russian industry grew. Mendeleev visited the United States in 1876. He observed the American petroleum industry, criticizing it for wastefulness. Interestingly, Russian-American competition apparently began long before the "Cold War" of the 1940's and 1950's.

Mendeleev also had a great interest in flight and made balloon flights to make scientific observations. He urged scientists and inventors to make a "heavier-than-air machine." (The airplane had not yet been invented nor had the name been coined.)

Dmitri Ivanovich Mendeleev was born in Tobolsk, Siberia, in 1834. Siberia is a vast, remote area of eastern Russia. Dmitri was the seventeenth child of middle-class parents. His father became blind when Dmitri was a boy, requiring the mother to support the family. When Dmitri's father died, his mother took Dmitri and a sister to Moscow. She wanted to enroll Dmitri in the university there. Unfortunately, Russian society was very rigid at that time. No place was made in the university for a young man from a remote area such as Siberia.

The Mendeleevs went on to St. Petersburg. This city, located on the Gulf of Finland, was the capital of Russia. (Today it is named Leningrad—the second-largest city in the Soviet Union, but no longer the capital.) St. Petersburg was a cultural city, the home of schools, colleges, and universities. Again, Dmitri was barred from the university. He did manage, however, to get into the Pedagogic Institute, a school for teachers. Shortly afterward, Dmitri's mother died.

Dmitri did well at the Pedagogic Institute. He won a gold medal for academic achievement. In 1855 he went to Odessa, in southern

Dmitri Mendeleev proposes a form of the periodic table of elements.

1869

reactionary. The czar still ruled the country with absolute power. Mendeleev got into trouble for speaking his mind freely. After a series of reprimands, Mendeleev was dismissed from his teaching position in 1890. He never held a college or university teaching job again.

Although retired from teaching, Mendeleev worked on several government projects. For instance, he worked in the Bureau of Weights and Measures for many years.

Mendeleev died in 1907. In his honor, a chemical element was named *mendelevium.* Mendelevium was created artificially during experiments on radioactive elements.

Dmitri Ivanovich Mendeleev, the Russian chemist, is pictured in a hot-air balloon studying the solar eclipse of 1887

Josiah Gibbs

Josiah Gibbs (1839-1903) was perhaps the greatest U.S. scientist before 1900. Although not understood or appreciated by his contemporaries, Gibbs made important contributions to the science of thermodynamics. Thermodynamics deals with forms of energy and conversion of energy from one form to another. The principles of thermodynamics can be applied to many uses. One use is the study of efficiency in machines. Another is calculation of energy loss or gain in chemical reactions.

Gibbs applied the principles of thermodynamics to physical chemistry. His work in this field has earned him the nickname, "the father of modern physical chemistry." One of Gibbs' most important contributions was his formulation of the *phase rule.* This is a logical description of the physical relationships among the different states of a substance, such as water, ice, and water vapor. Gibbs' most famous written work is *On the Equilibrium of Heterogeneous Substances,* published between 1875 and 1878 in the *Transactions of the Connecticut Academy.*

One of the great scientists of the age, physicist James Clerk Maxwell in England, recognized Josiah Gibbs' genius. But few Americans thought highly of him.

Josiah Gibbs was born into an academic New England family. His father was a professor at Yale University in New Haven, Connecticut. Josiah himself attended Yale University and in 1863 won the first doctorate of engineering awarded in the United States. After ex-

Russia, to take up a teaching appointment. He returned to St. Petersburg the next year to work on an advanced degree in chemistry. In 1859 the Russian government sent Mendeleev to the University of Heidelberg in southwestern Germany for further studies. While in Heidelberg, Mendeleev made valuable contacts with German, Italian, and French scientists.

Mendeleev returned to Russia in 1861. He did some writing and editing of scientific texts to earn a living. In 1864 he became a professor at the Technical Institute and in 1867, at the university in St. Petersburg—a position of prestige.

Mendeleev was a political thinker as well as scientist. He favored reform in the Russian government, which at the time was extremely

Josiah Gibbs develops and publishes the phase rule, explaining the relationships between gases, solids, and liquids.

 1875-1878

tended travels in Europe in the late 1860's, Gibbs returned to a professorship at Yale. There he spent the remaining years of his professional life.

Robert Koch

Robert Koch (1843-1910), a German scientist, firmly established the modern science of bacteriology. He proved that microbes, tiny, one-celled organisms, can cause disease in animals and humans. He developed precise methods for growing, observing, and preserving cultures (growths) of bacteria. He also isolated and identified many disease-causing microbes.

Most famous is Koch's work with anthrax, a disease that often infected sheep and cattle. Koch isolated the anthrax bacillus and cultivated it for observation. *(Bacillus* is a singular form of the word *bacteria.)* Eventually, Koch determined the entire life cycle of this microbe. He found that anthrax bacteria form spores that can survive outside of animal bodies and even dry out. Then, months or years later, the spores can reinfect animals. This discovery explained why sheep sometimes became infected with anthrax after grazing in fields that had been abandoned for years. Koch's thorough success in cultivating and studying anthrax bacteria enabled him to prove the link between the bacteria and the disease itself. This was a major breakthrough in medical science.

Koch also isolated and identified the bacillus that causes tuberculosis. A disease of the lungs, tuberculosis infected and killed many thousands of people in Koch's time. Koch announced this important discovery at the Physiological Society of Berlin in 1882. He worked to develop a serum to treat the disease. Although he produced such a serum in 1890, it proved ineffective as a cure. However, Koch's serum is used even today to diagnose tuberculosis.

Koch investigated many exotic diseases of Asia and Africa. He studied leprosy, bubonic plague, and malaria. Koch may have discovered the link between the spread of malaria and mosquito bites. But a British bacteriologist, Ronald Ross, made the same discovery, perhaps earlier, and published it. Sponsored

by the German government, Koch traveled to Egypt and India to investigate outbreaks of cholera. Cholera is a serious, often fatal disease of humans and animals. After much effort, Koch discovered the bacillus that causes cholera and the ways in which humans become infected. While in Egypt, he also discovered the organisms that cause certain kinds of dysentery (diarrhea) and conjunctivitis (eye infection).

Koch developed precise scientific techniques for growing, observing, and preserving microbes, such as bacteria. The modern science of bacteriology owes many of its methods to Koch. He invented the pure-culture technique of growing microbes. This involved the use of a sterilized gelatin called agar. One of Koch's techniques for observing microbes with a microscope is called the "hanging-drop" technique. In this technique, bacteria are grown in a drop of nutrient solution on the underside of a glass slide. Koch also developed photomicrographs, the technique of photographing an image, such as bacterial cells, as seen through the microscope. In 1877 Koch published a scientific paper on many of these techniques. It included fine examples of photomicrographs.

Koch also showed how microbes cause infections in wounds, and he identified specific microbes that cause such infections. This work gave theoretical support to the efforts of Joseph Lister and others in bringing antiseptic practices to hospital operating rooms.

Koch was an excellent teacher. Many of his students enjoyed distinguished and successful careers in bacteriology or related fields. His student Paul Ehrlich developed an effective treatment for syphilis. Another student, Shibasaburo Kitasato, developed an effective serum against bubonic plague.

Robert Koch was born in 1843 near Hannover in northern Germany. He studied medicine at the University of Göttingen, Germany, and received his medical degree in 1866. Koch served as a field surgeon in the Franco-Prussian War (1870-1871), then served as a surgeon in a provincial town where he set up his first laboratory.

By the late 1870's, Koch had established a reputation as a leading bacteriologist. He accepted a position at the German Health Office, which provided him a fully equipped laboratory. In 1885 Koch became a professor at the University of Berlin. He founded the Institute

An engraving, based upon an 1884 photograph, of **Robert Koch,** the German physician and bacteriologist

Robert Koch identifies the type of bacteria that causes tuberculosis.

1876   1882   1885

Robert Koch proves that bacteria cause anthrax, thereby proving the germ theory.

Louis Pasteur administers the first successful rabies vaccine.

for Infectious Diseases in Berlin in 1891.

For his work with tuberculosis bacteria, Koch won the 1905 Nobel Prize for physiology or medicine. He died in 1910.

In 1889 Hertz became a professor on the physics faculty of the University of Bonn in western Germany. Hertz died in 1894, not yet 40 years of age.

Heinrich Hertz

Heinrich Hertz (1857-1894) was a German physicist who did pioneering laboratory work with electromagnetic waves. These are waves of energy that radiate outward from a source of electrical or magnetic force into the space around the source. Radio waves, for example, are a type of electromagnetic wave. Hertz's experimental findings led to the development of radio in the decades after his death.

Hertz conducted his experiments on electromagnetic waves in the middle 1880's at the Karlsruhe Polytechnic, a German University where he was a faculty member. In 1883 Hertz began studying the electromagnetic theory of British physicist James Clerk Maxwell, who had died in 1879. Maxwell had predicted the existence of electromagnetic waves in the 1860's but had never proved his theory. Using Maxwell's ideas, Hertz set up a crude radio transmitter and receiver. His experiments confirmed that electromagnetic (radio) waves had passed through the air between two points.

Hertz conducted a number of experiments on the waves he had generated. He measured their length and determined their speed of movement. He also found that the waves could be reflected and refracted (bent) just as light waves. This finding persuaded Hertz that light is a kind of electromagnetic radiation, which James Clerk Maxwell had also predicted.

The theoretical work of James Clerk Maxwell and Hertz's laboratory experiments led eventually to many of the inventions we take for granted today. Some of these are radio, television, radar, satellite communications, and microwave ovens. Life in the twentieth century would be very different without the contributions of these scientists.

Heinrich Hertz was born in 1857 in Hamburg, a city in northwestern Germany. Hertz had a solid educational background in physics. While at the University of Berlin, he studied under the great German scientist, Hermann von Helmholtz. Hertz earned a Ph.D. with honors in 1880.

Shibasaburo Kitasato

Shibasaburo Kitasato (1852-1931) was a Japanese physician and bacteriologist who made important discoveries about bacterial diseases and contributed to knowledge of their treatment. Kitasato became thoroughly trained in medical knowledge and techniques then being developed in Germany. For several years, Kitasato worked at Robert Koch's laboratory in Berlin, along with the famous bacteriologist Emil von Behring. He brought the new ideas from Germany to Japan and continued research in his native country and East Asia after 1892.

At the Koch laboratory in Germany, Kitasato did research on the bacteria that cause tetanus and diphtheria. Tetanus, often called "lockjaw"—it causes the muscles to become rigid—sometimes strikes a person who has received a deep cut or puncture. It is a serious, often fatal, disease. Diphtheria, also often fatal, infected and killed many children in Kitasato's time.

In 1889 Kitasato obtained a pure culture, or growth, of the tetanus bacillus. (*Bacillus* is a singular form of the word *bacteria.*) He was the first bacteriologist to do so. In 1890 Kitasato and Emil von Behring showed how blood serum taken from an animal infected with tetanus could be used to produce immunity in a healthy human or animal. Immunity is the ability of a living organism to fight off infection.

In 1894, Kitasato had a unique, if gruesome, opportunity to study bubonic plague when an epidemic broke out in Hong Kong. Bubonic plague is a severe disease that kills, if left untreated, most of the people it infects. During the Middle Ages in Europe, it had wiped out one-third to one-half of the population within a few years. Periodically it returned, especially in places with poor nutrition, housing, and sanitation. Kitasato conducted intensive research on this disease. He soon discovered the bacillus that causes bubonic plague. (The French bacteriologist Alexandre Yersin made

Heinrich Hertz discovers electromagnetic waves.

Sir William Osler publishes his discovery of human blood platelets.

| 1886-1887 | 1887 | 1891 | ca. 1894 |

Albert Michelson and **Edward Morley** devise an experiment that disproves the existence of *ether*, an invisible, elastic substance formerly supposed to fill all space.

Shibasaburo Kitasato discovers the bacillus that causes bubonic plague.

the same discovery at about the same time.) Eventually, Kitasato developed a serum that helps protect people from infection by bubonic plague.

Kitasato studied the ways in which the tuberculosis bacillus infects people. He also showed how dead cultures of disease-causing microbes (germs) could be used in vaccinations.

In 1899, Kitasato founded a laboratory near Tokyo that was modeled on Koch's bacteriological laboratory. The Japanese government eventually sponsored and funded it as the Imperial Japanese Institute for the Study of Infectious Diseases. In 1914 Kitasato resigned from the Imperial Japanese Institute and founded the Kitasato Institute, his own research laboratory.

Kitasato was born in Kumamoto, Japan, in 1852. In the next year, Japan was opened to trade and contact with the West. Kitasato was one of an increasing number of Japanese to bring Western ideas and technology to Japan.

After a long, productive career, Shibasaburo Kitasato died in 1931.

Wilhelm Roentgen

Wilhelm Roentgen (1845-1923) was the German physicist who discovered X rays in 1895. For his work with X rays, Roentgen won the 1901 Nobel Prize in physics.

In late 1895, Roentgen was conducting experiments with a Crookes tube. A Crookes tube is a pear-shaped vacuum tube with a positive terminal (anode) and a negative terminal (cathode). The cathode could be supplied with a high-voltage electrical current. When electrical power was thus supplied, the tube glowed.

In a variation of the experiment, Roentgen wrapped the Crookes tube in heavy black paper. When electric current was supplied, Roentgen noticed that a fluorescent screen nearby glowed. Roentgen found that he could cast "shadows" on the screen by putting metal objects between the Crookes tube and the fluorescent screen. He determined that some unknown rays—"X rays"—were travelling outward from the Crookes tube.

Roentgen performed a rapid series of follow-up experiments. He found that the X

Wilhelm Roentgen, German physicist, lectures on his discovery of the X ray

Wilhelm Roentgen
discovers X rays.

1895

Guglielmo Marconi
transmits the first telegraphic signal through air.

rays travel in straight lines and that they pass through some objects (paper, skin, wood) while not through others (bones, metals). He also discovered that X rays affect photographic plates, that is, X rays can "take pictures." On December 22, 1895, Roentgen took an X-ray photograph of his wife's hand. This image clearly showed the bone structures in her hand. It demonstrated the important medical uses to which X rays could be put.

X rays are used in many areas of medicine today, including diagnosis and treatment (destruction of cancer cells, for instance). They have also proved an extremely valuable tool for studying the molecular structure of substances. In a technique called X-ray diffraction, scientists can determine the arrangement of atoms and molecules in crystals.

Roentgen's work had a powerful impact on the physicists of his time. His discovery of X rays encouraged other scientists, such as Henri Becquerel and the Curies, to investigate other types of invisible radiation.

Roentgen also conducted experiments on the behavior of electricity in crystals. He investigated the specific heat of gases.

Wilhelm Roentgen was born in western Germany in 1845. He studied at the Polytechnic Institute in Zürich and at the universities of Strasbourg and Würzburg. He taught physics at the University of Giessen and at the University of Würzburg. From 1900 to 1920 he taught at the University of Munich. Roentgen died in 1923.

Antoine Henri Becquerel

Antoine Henri Becquerel (1852-1908) was a French physicist who discovered radioactivity and identified some of the properties of radioactive materials. For his work on radioactivity, Becquerel shared the 1903 Nobel Prize in physics with Marie and Pierre Curie.

In 1895, William Roentgen, a German physicist, discovered X rays. Roentgen's discovery stimulated a great deal of interest in invisible radiation. Scientists wondered if other types of invisible radiation existed.

Henri Becquerel wanted to know if he could establish any connection between visible and invisible radiation. He devised an experiment to test this idea. In his experiment,

Becquerel wrapped a photographic plate in many layers of heavy paper. He then put a phosphorescent crystal on the wrapped plate and illuminated it with light. (A phosphorescent substance radiates light after being exposed to light.) When Becquerel later examined the photographic plate, he saw the shadow of the crystal.

At first, Becquerel thought that the shadowy image on the photographic plate was caused by the action of light on the experimental substance, a uranium compound. But then he noticed that the substance produced a photographic image even when it had not been exposed to light. The radiation seemed to come from the substance without any external action. In 1896 and 1897, Becquerel published several papers on his experiments.

Pierre and Marie Curie followed up on Becquerel's discovery. They worked with thorium, a radioactive element. Then they discovered new radioactive elements, radium and polonium.

Then Becquerel returned his attention to radioactivity, building on the advances made by the Curies. He measured the deflection of Beta particles caused by electrical and magnetic fields. Beta rays are a type of radiation given off by radioactive elements, such as radium. From these experiments, Becquerel concluded that Beta particles are electrons. Becquerel also noticed a change in the level of radiation in uranium over time. He realized that the element uranium was undergoing a transformation through its radioactivity. In a few years, Ernest Rutherford was to work out the transformation theory of radioactivity.

Becquerel was also the first scientist to write about the effects of radiation on living tissue. He suffered radiation burns on his own body from carrying a lump of radium in a pocket. Becquerel reported this discovery in 1901.

Henri Becquerel was born in 1852 of a famous French scientific family. He attended the Polytechnic School and the School of Bridges and Highways in Paris. For many years, Becquerel worked as an engineer in the French Department of Bridges and Highways as well as an experimental physicist. Becquerel also taught physics at the Polytechnic School.

Becquerel was elected to the French Academy of Sciences in 1889. He became the president of the Academy shortly before his death in 1908.

Antoine Henri Becquerel discovers natural radioactivity.

 1896

Sir Joseph John Thomson

Sir Joseph John Thomson (1856-1940) was the British physicist who discovered the electron, a fundamental atomic particle. Thomson received the 1906 Nobel Prize in physics for this work.

In the middle 1890's, Thomson conducted a series of experiments on cathode rays. These rays are produced in a vacuum tube equipped with a positive terminal (anode) and a negative terminal (cathode). The cathode rays result when high-voltage electrical current is supplied to the cathode.

Thomson believed that cathode rays were actually streams of tiny charged particles. He devised experiments to deflect, or bend, the cathode rays from their normal path in the tube. Then he worked out mathematical calculations on the experimental data. Thomson concluded that the rays were indeed composed of tiny charged particles, which he named "corpuscles." Later, the name "electron" was adopted. Thomson demonstrated that the particles are negatively charged, can generate heat, and have very little mass—about 1,000 times less mass than a hydrogen ion (proton), in fact. Furthermore, Thomson showed through repeated experiments that electrons are present in many chemical elements. And he theorized (correctly) that electrons are a fundamental part of all matter.

Thomson's discovery revolutionized scientific understanding of the atom. Before Thomson, most scientists had believed that the atom was indivisible, the smallest particle of matter that could exist. His work proved that the atom could indeed be broken down into smaller particles. For this reason, Thomson can be considered the founder of modern atomic physics.

Based on his work with electrons, Thomson proposed an atomic model. He suggested that the atom is a sphere (a round ball) with the electrons embedded throughout its inner volume. According to Thomson's model, the interior of an atom would resemble a watermelon with embedded seeds. Within the following 20 years, however, physicists Ernest Rutherford and Niels Bohr would develop a more workable atomic model.

Thomson discovered the first isotopes of a chemical element, specifically of the element neon. An isotope is a form of a chemical element that has a different atomic weight than the element in its normal form. Later, a pupil of Thomson, Francis Aston, invented the mass spectrograph. This device separates atoms of differing atomic weights in a substance.

In 1903 Thomson proposed a discontinuous theory of light. By this, Thomson meant that light rays are composed of separate particles rather than continuous streams. Several years later, Einstein developed the photon theory of light. This theory proposes that light is made up of packets of energy called *photons*.

Thomson had a great impact on the field of atomic physics as a teacher. He was director of the Cavendish Laboratory at Cambridge University for the eventful years in the 1890's and early 1900's. During this period, modern atomic physics came into being. Under Thomson's leadership, the Cavendish Laboratory became a world center for atomic physics research. He guided a generation of great physicists, including Ernest Rutherford, who established modern atomic theory. In all, seven of Thomson's students—including his own son, Sir George Paget Thomson—won Nobel Prizes.

Thomson was a natural teacher. He believed teaching to be an essential part of research. According to Thomson, the process of teaching allowed him to refine and clarify his own ideas and theories. Without the opportunity to teach, he thought, a scientist's ideas might become too rigid and inflexible.

Joseph John Thomson was born in 1856 near Manchester, England. He entered college at the age of 14. In 1876 he entered Cambridge University. He began working in the Cavendish Laboratory in 1880 and became its chief professor four years later. Thomson spent the rest of his professional life at the Cavendish Laboratory. Thomson traveled and lectured in the United States on several occasions. He lectured at Princeton in 1896 and at Yale in 1903.

Many honors and awards came to Thomson during his long, productive life. In addition to his Nobel Prize, Thomson won the Order of Merit in 1912. He was knighted by King Edward VII in 1908. Thomson also participated in many scientific societies. He was made a member of the Royal Society of London in 1884. For several years, he served as president of the British Association for the Advancement of Science.

Thomson remained deeply involved in the Cavendish Laboratory and Cambridge until his death in 1940 at the age of 83.

1897

Sir Joseph John Thomson
discovers the electron.

Pierre Curie

Pierre Curie (1859-1906), with his wife, Marie, conducted fundamental research and produced landmark discoveries in the field of radioactivity. Pierre Curie's life ended early and tragically when, in April, 1906, he was killed by a speeding wagon in the streets of Paris. Thus, one of the most brilliant scientific careers of modern times was prematurely terminated.

Pierre Curie demonstrated brilliance at an early age. By the time he was 18, Pierre was working as a laboratory assistant at the Sorbonne in Paris. At about this time, he conducted his first important original research—calculating wavelengths of heat waves. With his brother Jacques, Pierre then conducted intensive and significant studies of crystal structures. In the course of their work, the Curie brothers discovered piezoelectricity, a type of electricity that is generated on a crystal by a change of temperature.

In 1882 Pierre Curie was appointed supervisor at the School of Industrial Physics and Chemistry in Paris. During this period, Curie carried out important experiments in magnetism. He discovered the basic principle relating magnetic attraction and temperature—Curie's law. This work led to discovery of the Curie point, the temperature at which some magnetic materials experience a sudden change of magnetic properties.

Pierre Curie met Marie Sklodowska in 1894, and they were married in July, 1895. Thus began the most celebrated husband-wife scientific team in history. Pierre's and Marie's collaboration produced a number of major scientific discoveries in rapid succession. Their scientific curiosity had been spurred by Henri Becquerel's discovery of radioactivity in 1896. They turned their attention to pitchblende (uranium ore). By 1898 they had isolated the radioactive elements radium and polonium. While Marie concentrated on isolation of further elements, Pierre undertook a study of the physical properties of the radioactive elements. By applying magnetic fields to the rays given off by radium, he showed that such rays include particles that are charged positively, negatively, and neutrally (that is, containing no charge). These rays of the different particles would later be named alpha, beta, and gamma rays.

Pierre Curie also studied the effects of radioactivity on living tissue. His work laid the groundwork for radiation therapy in medicine.

Pierre Curie became a lecturer at the Sorbonne in 1900 and full professor in 1904. His wife assumed the Sorbonne professorship after Pierre's death in 1906. The Curies won several prizes and honors, including the 1903 Nobel Prize, shared with Becquerel. In 1903 they also received the Royal Society's Davy Medal. Pierre was elected to the prestigious Academy of Sciences in 1905.

A 1896 photograph of **Marie** and **Pierre Curie** in their Paris laboratory

Pierre and **Marie Curie** isolate the radioactive element, radium.

1898

Marie Curie

Marie Curie (1867-1934) was a Polish-born French physicist who made fundamental discoveries in the field of radioactivity, first in collaboration with her husband, Pierre, then on her own. For her pioneering work, Marie Curie won two Nobel Prizes, one shared with her husband and physicist Henri Becquerel in 1903 and a second, won alone in 1911.

Marie and Pierre Curie became interested in radioactive substances soon after Becquerel discovered radioactivity in 1896. The Curies discovered the radioactive elements polonium (named after Marie Curie's native land, Poland) and radium in 1898. The shared 1903 Nobel Prize was awarded to the Curies and Becquerel for the discovery of radioactivity. The Curies continued their research into radioactive elements and their properties.

The death of her husband on April 19, 1906, was a terrible blow to Marie Curie. Yet her decision to continue the work they had started guaranteed for Madame Curie a reputation equal to or surpassing her husband's.

In May, 1906, Madame Curie was appointed to her husband's vacant professorship at the Sorbonne in Paris. She was the first woman to teach at that university. In 1910, Curie published her fundamental treatise on radioactivity. Curie's 1911 Nobel Prize in chemistry was awarded for her work in isolating pure radium.

Madame Curie directed the work at the Institute of Radium at the University of Paris. Buildings were constructed in 1914, and the laboratory became fully operational in 1918. This laboratory became a major center for research in the fields of nuclear physics and chemistry.

By the 1920's Marie Curie had become widely known and highly popular as a leading scientist of the time. She traveled to many parts of the world, including the United States, where President Warren G. Harding received her in 1921. Furthermore, Madame Curie assumed a public role in such activities as membership on the International Commission on Intellectual Co-operation of the League of Nations.

During the same period, Curie remained active as a scientist. She devoted much of her scientific efforts during World War I and in later life to medical applications of radioactive substances. (She had become a member of the Academy of Medicine in 1922.) Curie also took care to stockpile radioactive substances at the Institute of Radium. The accumulation of these materials proved critical to ongoing scientific work in the field of radioactivity.

The Curies' oldest daughter, Irène, added to the illustrious reputation of the Curie family. With her physicist husband, Frédéric Joliot, Irène conducted further original research in the field of radioactivity. In 1934 the Joliot-Curies demonstrated that radioactive substances could be artificially produced. For this work they won the 1935 Nobel Prize in chemistry.

Marie Curie died in 1934 of leukemia, a disease that was probably induced by her work with radioactive materials, such as radium.

Max Planck, the German physicist, proposed the quantum theory in 1900

Max Planck

Max Planck (1858-1947) proposed the *quantum theory* in 1900 to explain how radiant energy (such as light) is given off and absorbed. The quantum theory completely revolutionized modern physics. It answered many questions and solved many problems that had puzzled scientists for years. For his work with the quantum theory, Planck won the Nobel Prize in physics in 1918.

The basic concept of the quantum theory is that radiant energy, such as light, is a continuous stream of tiny packets of energy called *quanta* (or *quantum* in the singular). A quantum is the smallest amount of energy possible. Mathematically, the energy in a quantum is measured as the frequency of the radiation, v, times a universal constant, h. This constant value is also known as *Planck's constant.* Planck's formula applies to all forms of radiant energy, including ultraviolet light, X rays, radio waves, microwaves, and so on. An obvious conclusion that can be drawn from Planck's theory (and formula) is that forms of radiant energy with high frequencies have higher energy than those with lower frequencies.

Planck proposed his theory to solve a particular experimental problem. He never expected it to become the basic principle of a new kind of physics. But this is exactly what happened. Albert Einstein and Niels Bohr

Early Twentieth Century——1900-1949

Max Planck originates the quantum theory.

 1900

Sigmund Freud publishes *The Interpretation of Dreams,* a landmark treatise on psychotherapy.

quickly adopted Planck's ideas and extended them to many areas of physics. Einstein used the quantum theory to explain the photoelectric effect. Bohr used the theory to explain how electrons in the outer shells of their atoms give off light energy without falling back into the nucleus. He theorized that electrons give off energy in limited bursts of quanta—not continuously.

Max Planck was born in Kiel, a city in northwestern Germany, in 1858. He studied at the universities of Munich and Berlin with the great German scientists Hermann Helmholtz and Gustav Kirchhoff. Planck received a Ph.D. in physics and began teaching physics at the university level. He taught at the University of Berlin for most of his career.

Planck served in many scientific associations, including the Prussian Academy of Science and the Kaiser Wilhelm Society of Berlin (later renamed the Max Planck Society). He was also made a foreign member of the Royal Society of London.

Planck enjoyed a wide range of interests outside of physics, including music, religion, and philosophy. He was also deeply concerned about justice. Planck stayed in Germany during the Nazi regime because he felt it his duty to do so. But his family suffered terribly. In 1944 his son Erwin was arrested and executed for alleged participation in the plot to assassinate Hitler. Planck remained in Germany after World War II. He died in 1947.

Sigmund Freud

Sigmund Freud (1856-1939) was the founder of psychoanalysis, a therapy for treating mental or emotional disturbances. Moreover, Freud formulated a body of theory on how the mind works. Freud's theory has revolutionized modern understanding of the human mind and how it affects behavior. Almost every area of human activity—including art, psychology, education, criminology, sexuality—has been touched in some way by Freud's ideas.

Freud established psychoanalysis, sometimes called "the talking cure," as a fundamental therapy for treating people with mental or emotional disturbances. He gathered disciples and originated a school of thought in psychol-

ogy. Eventually, some of his disciples broke with him and formed their own schools of psychology. Today, many psychologists and psychiatrists disagree with particular aspects of Freud's theories. But all acknowledge their debt to him in laying a theoretical foundation for the study and treatment of the mind.

Freud's psychological theory was developed gradually over his long and active career and explained in a large number of writings. His first important insights about the mind came in the 1890's. At the time, he was treating patients suffering from a mental illness called *hysteria.* People suffering from hysteria have physical ailments, such as blindness or paralysis, for which no physical cause can be found. The French neurologist, Jean Martin Charcot, demonstrated in 1885 that the cause of hysteria is mental disturbance. Freud was studying with Charcot at this time. He returned to Vienna, his home, to work with hysterical patients.

From this work came many insights. During this period, Freud laid the ground theory of psychoanalysis. In psychoanalysis, the analyst—the psychiatrist or psychologist who works with the patient—encourages the patient to talk. The patient gradually shares much self-revealing information. At first, however, the patient's mind puts up many defense mechanisms. This is because the mind has *repressed,* that is, buried, painful thoughts or experiences far from conscious awareness. The area of the mind in which such ideas and feelings are buried is called *the subconscious.* We are not usually aware of the subconscious, but it often becomes more transparent at night, during dreams. For this reason, Freud's treatment included interpretation of dreams. Freud also developed a technique called *free association* to gain information from the subconscious. In free association, the analyst has the patient talk on and on, saying the first thoughts that come into the mind. Sometimes the free association is directed. For example, the analyst may show the patient ink blots and ask the patient to state an interpretation.

The condition in which thoughts and feelings are repressed is called *neurosis.* People suffering from neurosis may act in illogical, repetitive, or even harmful ways. According to psychoanalytic theory, the patient begins to be cured when most of the repressed thoughts are brought to the conscious mind. But this healing process occurs only gradually, usually over a long period of time.

Hugo de Vries publishes his mutation theory of evolution.

Christiaan Eijkman and **Frederick Hopkins** demonstrate the existence of vitamins.

1900-1903   **1902**   **ca. 1903**

Wilheim Wien discovers the atomic proton.

A circa 1930 photograph of **Sigmund Freud** in the office of his house in Vienna

Some of Freud's most shocking and controversial theories concern human sexuality. As Freud developed his practice, he became convinced that sexual fears lay at the heart of many mental and emotional disturbances. He believed that sexual desires begin in infancy and continue throughout life. Freud mapped out stages of sexual development and described the emotional state of each stage. He devised theories to explain how progression of family members through these sexual stages affect their relationships with each other. These changing family relationships in turn affect the mental and emotional development of the children in the family.

Most psychologists and psychiatrists today place less emphasis on sexuality in treatment of emotional and mental disturbances than did Freud. Furthermore, we now know that Freud's understanding of sexuality was influenced by his personal relationships, especially to his parents, and by his own male bias. Still, Freud's theories prepared the way for a deeper understanding of human sexuality and its effect on emotional development. To this day, his thinking profoundly affects the way we regard sexuality.

As he elaborated his theories, Freud continued to refine the techniques of psychotherapy. He came to believe that patients often transfer repressed feelings they have had toward people in their lives to the analyst. Such feelings may include love, hate, sexual desire, and many others. Freud called this process *transference*. Because he considered it such an important technique of psychoanalysis, Freud encouraged transference in his patients. One way he did this was to have the patient lie on a couch during psychoanalysis. This technique would help the patient fantasize that the analyst was really someone else, the object of the patient's strong emotions.

Clinical experience has shown most of the psychoanalytic techniques developed by Freud to be sound. Free association, dream interpretation, and transference continue to be used today.

Sir William Ramsay receives the Nobel Prize in chemistry for isolating argon, helium, neon, krypton, and xenon.

1904

Freud continued to develop a theoretical understanding of how the mind works. He devised the theory of a three-part division of the mind. He named these parts the *id,* the *ego,* and the *superego.* The id is the mental representation of basic biological instincts. Such instincts include the drive to satisfy hunger and the drive to satisfy sexual needs. The id, the most primitive part of the human mind, is unconcerned with external reality. Another part of the mind, the ego—a Latin word meaning "I"—connects mental images with the outside world. The ego allows each of us to relate to the people and the world around us. Without it, we would live in a reality driven wholly by our primitive instincts. The third part of the mind, the superego, is the internal, mental representation of society's moral demands. It begins to develop as young children are disciplined by their parents.

Freud's theoretical model of the human mind contributed a much deeper understanding of how the mind works. Before Freud's pioneering work in this field, little had really been understood about the mind. The very fact that Freud's own words for parts of the mind—id, ego, and superego—have passed into everyday language indicates his great impact on our thinking.

In later life, Freud applied his theories to an examination of human society and culture. Freud theorized that the creation and appreciation of beauty, as in art, is really the sublimation of certain sexual desires. *Sublimation* means submerging or burying. Whereas repression of such feelings in an individual can lead to neurosis and illness, sublimation through art is a positive activity.

Freud also attempted to explain why people join together in societies. He suggested that the roots of modern society lay in primitive urges to gather into a group and to give up control to a dominant father figure. He also theorized that religious experience is an attempt to return to the earliest stage of life, when a baby feels at one with its mother. These ideas have remained very controversial.

Sigmund Freud was born in Moravia (now Czechoslovakia) of Jewish parents in 1856. The Freud family moved frequently during Sigmund's early childhood, but eventually settled in Vienna.

As a young man, Freud decided to enter the field of medicine. He graduated from the medical school of the University of Vienna in 1881. Later, Freud decided to specialize in *neurology,* the study and treatment of disorders of the nervous system. In 1885 Freud went to Paris to study with the famous neurologist, Jean Charcot. He returned to Vienna in 1886 and started his own clinical work.

Over a period of 30 years or more, Freud developed and revised his psychological theories. In 1923, he began to suffer from cancer of the mouth.

In 1938 the German Nazis under Hitler arranged for Austria to be annexed to Germany. Freud and his family, as Jews, feared for their safety. They fled to England, where Freud died of cancer in 1939.

Freud's daughter, Anna, followed her father in the field of psychoanalysis. She developed theories on child psychology and treated children with emotional and mental disturbances. Anna Freud established the Hampstead Child Therapy Course and Clinic in London and continued her work there for many years. She died in 1982.

Sigmund Freud wrote an enormous number of books and articles setting forth his various theories. Among the most important of them are *The Interpretation of Dreams* (1900), *Three Essays on the Theory of Sexuality* (1905), *Totem and Taboo* (1913), *General Introduction to Psychoanalysis* (1920), *The Ego and the Id* (1923), and *Civilization and its Discontents* (1930).

Albert Einstein

Albert Einstein (1879-1955) was one of the greatest scientists and most creative minds of all time. Before he was 30 years old, Einstein had published a group of brilliant theories that completely changed modern science. His theories provided basic knowledge needed to unleash the power of the atom. Einstein urged the United States to prepare to stop Nazi Germany by developing an atomic weapon. Then, after the Nazi threat was gone, he urged nations to join together in a world government that would, he believed, use atomic power responsibly.

Einstein revealed several of his earth-shaking theories in the single year of 1905. He presented his ideas in three scientific papers pub-

Albert Einstein proposes the theory of relativity and a theory explaining the photoelectric effect.

 1905

Ernest Rutherford theorizes that the half-life of radioactive minerals could be used to determine the age of minerals.

lished in *Annals of Physics,* a German physics journal.

One of the papers of 1905 was entitled, "On a Heuristic Viewpoint Concerning the Production and Transformation of Light." Einstein suggested that light could be thought of as a stream of tiny particles, called *quanta.* For this reason, light demonstrates qualities of both

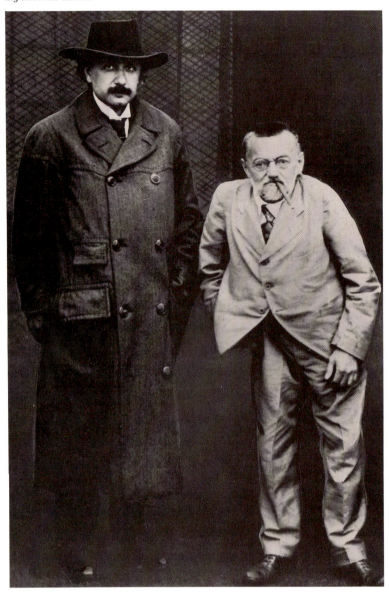

A photograph of **Albert Einstein** (l.) with fellow scientist Charles Steinmetz, shortly after Einstein proposed his general theory of relativity; Steinmetz developed the theory of alternating electrical current.

waves and particles. Einstein's ideas about light laid important groundwork for the quantum theory of physics. The quantum theory would become, in a short time, a revolutionary way of thinking about motion at the atomic level. Einstein also explained the photoelectric effect. This occurs when a bright beam of light strikes certain metal, causing the metal to release electrons in the form of an electrical current. Einstein's work made possible the development of the photoelectric cell, also called the electric eye. The 1921 Nobel Prize in physics was awarded to Einstein for this work.

Another paper of 1905, "The Electrodynamics of Moving Bodies," presented Einstein's special theory of relativity. This theory introduced the following idea: given that the speed of light is constant and all natural laws are the same, then both time and motion are relative to the observer. This was a radical change in scientific thinking, because no one had yet thought that time or motion might be subjective, that is changeable depending upon the observer's perspective.

Later in the same year, Einstein published another closely related paper. He worked out some of the mathematical ideas related to special relativity. Most importantly, he related mass to energy in a definite proportion in his famous equation,

$$E = mc^2$$

in which *E* stands for energy, *m* for mass, and *c* for the speed of light. The equation implied that an enormous amount of energy could be liberated from a relatively small amount of matter. It established the theoretical foundation for later work with atomic power.

Still another Einstein paper of 1905 was "On the Motion of Small Particles Suspended in a Stationary Liquid." In this paper, Einstein explained the apparently random motion of tiny particles in a liquid. This type of motion is known in science as Brownian motion.

Some years later, Einstein developed his theory of relativity more broadly. In 1916 he published an article entitled, "The Foundation of the General Theory of Relativity," in *Annals of Physics.* Einstein explained that gravitation is a curved field in the space-time continuum, rather than a force as Sir Isaac Newton had thought. Theoretically, this meant that starlight should be bent, or deflected, as it passes by the sun. But there was no immediate way to test Einstein's theory, since doing so would require observations at the time of a solar eclipse. That is the only time in which starlight is visible to observers on the earth.

Proof of Einstein's general theory of relativity came in 1919. In that year, the Royal Society of London sent a scientific expedition to the Principe Island in the Gulf of Guinea to observe a solar eclipse. The sun's eclipse allowed the scientists to observe starlight passing near the sun. Their calculations verified Einstein's predictions.

Confirmation of Einstein's theory of relativity brought him international and lasting fame. From this time on, Einstein belonged to the world. Moreover, the very name of Einstein became a synonym for genius. Few scientists have become as widely or as popularly known in life as Einstein.

From the 1920's on, Einstein directed his scientific efforts toward finding mathematical relationships that would unify all kinds of forces, such as gravity and electromagnetism. This new field of research became known as unified field theory. Einstein's efforts in this field drew him into controversy. Many, if not most, physicists believed that the quest for a unified field theory was an impossible one. They reasoned that the movement of a single particle cannot be predicted, according to the quantum theory. For the most part, they also believed that future theoretical advances in physics would never remove this basic uncertainty principle. For these reasons, Einstein became rather isolated from the scientific community toward the end of his life.

Einstein lived a very public life in his mature years. This was, in part, a result of the extraordinary fame he achieved in science. Also, world events repeatedly forced Einstein into the limelight. At various times of his life, Einstein had been a German, Swiss, and United States citizen. He had lived through the two world wars as a mature man. Furthermore, Einstein had passionate opinions on war, peace, and world government.

During World War I, Einstein had risked grave trouble by embracing pacifism, a belief in peace at almost any cost. Einstein also supported Zionism—the movement to created a homeland for the Jewish people in Palestine. Later, he supported the state of Israel.

Einstein continued to be a pacifist until Hitler gained power in Germany. In 1933 Einstein renounced his German citizenship and fled Germany. Shortly afterward, he accepted a position at Princeton University in the United States. He was to live at Princeton for the rest of his life.

A group of physicists persuaded Einstein to write a letter of warning to President Roosevelt in 1939. The content of this warning was that the uranium atom had been split, and Hitler's scientists might be developing an atomic bomb. President Roosevelt took Einstein's letter—signed by several prominent scientists—quite seriously. Shortly afterward, he took steps to commit the United States to developing an atomic weapon. This was the beginning of the Manhattan project and the bombs used on Japan in 1945. Einstein himself took no part in the project. Ironically, he learned of the atomic attacks against Hiroshima and Nagasaki in August, 1945, in the same ways as most Americans—through radio and newspapers.

Always a public figure, Einstein joined with other scientists in urging the responsible use of atomic energy. Einstein had a particular vision of a peaceful postwar era. He wanted the former Allies—the United States, Britain, and the Soviet Union—to establish a world government. Such a government, believed Einstein, would have the authority to control the use of atomic power. By the late 1940's, a bitter cold war had developed between the United States and the Soviet Union. Einstein's hopes for world unity were dashed.

Nevertheless, Einstein continued his work in physics with unified field theory. He published a version of the theory in 1950.

Albert Einstein was born in southern Germany in 1879. As a boy, Einstein went to the rigid, harsh German schools of the late 1800's. Young Albert showed little scholastic ability. Meanwhile, he studied the violin with his Uncle Jacob. Thus, Einstein began a lifelong enjoyment of music as a very good amateur violinist. Einstein later said that music first stimulated his fascination with mathematics.

In 1900 Einstein graduated from the Swiss Polytechnic Academy in Zürich, Switzerland and became a Swiss citizen. A short time later he married and got a job at the Swiss Patent Office. Einstein published his famous scientific papers in 1905. Einstein's astonishing theories earned him respect from the scientific community. He won teaching positions at European universities, first at Prague, then Zürich,

Albert Einstein photographed at Princeton University, where he lived and worked after fleeing Nazi Germany

Élie Metchnikoff
discovered the function of phagocytes in blood.

ca. 1905

and finally at Berlin in 1914. During this time Einstein was separated from his wife and family by the outbreak of war. The separation led to the couple's divorce.

After the war, Einstein married his cousin Elsa. She remained with him until her death in 1936.

From the end of World War I through the rest of his life, Einstein was drawn more and more into theoretical physics. At the same time, he became more and more a public figure and citizen of the world. Albert Einstein died on April 18, 1955. People throughout the world mourned his passing. Einstein had made unequaled contributions to human understanding of the universe. Scientists and thinkers agreed that he was one of the greatest scientists of all time. Einstein had also worked hard for peace and understanding among the nations of the world. Although these efforts failed to achieve positive results in his lifetime, the people of the world recognized Einstein's great humanity.

Élie Metchnikoff

A 1923 photograph of **Ernest Rutherford,** who discovered the basic principles of radioactivity

Élie Metchnikoff (1845-1916) was an important Russian biologist. Metchnikoff discovered the function of phagocytes in the blood. A *phagocyte* is a white blood cell that attacks disease-causing germs. For his work on phagocytes, Metchnikoff shared the 1908 Nobel Prize in medicine or physiology. Metchnikoff also conducted some of the earliest studies in the process of aging.

Metchnikoff showed how phagocytes attack, engulf, and destroy harmful germs such as bacteria. He also claimed that inflammation in a wound is caused by the struggle between phagocytes and the invading germs. Metchnikoff's writings on this topic include *Lectures on the Comparative Pathology of Inflammation* and *Immunity in Infective Diseases.*

Metchnikoff, working with Emile Roux at the Pasteur Institute in Paris, also did important experimental work with syphilis, a highly destructive disease that is sexually transmitted.

One of Metchnikoff's major scientific interests was the process of aging in humans. Metchnikoff observed people from the steppes region of central Russia, who tended to live very long lives. He believed that life style and diet were the key factors in long life. He advocated eating large amounts of cultured dairy products, such as yogurt. Metchnikoff believed that most people could live to an age of 150 years under the right conditions. He presented these ideas in a book entitled *The Prolongation of Life.*

Élie Metchnikoff was born in 1845 in the Ukraine region of Russia. He lived and worked in Russia until the late 1880's, when he went to the Pasteur Institute in Paris. Metchnikoff became a staff member of the Pasteur Institute in 1892 and its subdirector in 1895. Metchnikoff died in Paris in 1916.

Lord Ernest Rutherford

Lord Ernest Rutherford (1871-1937) was one of the greatest physicists of modern times. For his wide-ranging work in nuclear physics, Rutherford is known as the father of nuclear science. He discovered the basic principles of radioactivity, experimentally established the nuclear theory of the atom, and achieved the first artificial disintegration of a chemical element. Furthermore, he deeply influenced several generations of physicists—including those who eventually unlocked the secrets of atomic energy. Rutherford enjoyed a long, eventful career in physics. He served the scientific community well and received many honors.

Although a native of New Zealand, Rutherford earned a scholarship to do graduate work with J. J. Thomson, the great English physicist, at Cambridge University. Professor at the Cavendish Laboratory, Thomson was interested in radiation, specifically X rays, just then discovered by William Roentgen.

Rutherford joined Thomson in research on the effect of X rays on gases. They discovered that X rays produce strongly charged atoms in the gas (ions) that eventually recombine and neutralize each other. Rutherford found a way to measure the rate of recombination. He wrote a paper on the subject that received much attention.

In 1896, French physicist Henri Becquerel discovered that the element uranium gives off radiation. Rutherford identified the new types of radiation, which were different from X rays. He named them *alpha rays* and *beta rays.*

Ernest Rutherford confirms the existence of the proton in the atomic nucleus.

 1906

Rutherford continued his study of radiation, venturing into an uncharted area of physics. He eventually laid down the basic principles for the new field, known as radioactivity. Rutherford and his assistants studied three radioactive elements—radium, thorium, and actinium. They concluded that the atoms of a radioactive element disintegrate (break down) into the atoms of a different element. The new atoms are also radioactive. This was a radical new idea, for all previous atomic theory had held that atoms cannot be reduced.

Rutherford published his conclusions in *Radio-activity* (1904). He was elected to the Royal Society in 1903 and awarded the Rumford Medal in 1904 for this work. Later, in 1908, he won the Nobel Prize in chemistry.

Rutherford continued to work experimentally with alpha and beta rays. By observing the way they are deflected by magnetic and electrical fields, he discovered that alpha rays have a positive charge. He also determined their velocity.

Next Rutherford and his assistant, Hans Geiger, developed an apparatus (the Geiger counter) to measure the number of charged particles given off by radium. Using this device, Rutherford was able to determine Avogadro's number in the substance given off by the radium. (Avogadro's number is the constant number of molecules in the molecular weight in grams of a substance.) He also eventually proved that the alpha particle is really a helium atom.

Continuing his work with alpha particles in 1911, Rutherford made a profoundly important discovery. He produced a particular deflection of alpha particles that could be explained in only one way. Apparently all of the positive charge and almost all the mass of the atom was concentrated in a tiny region at its center. From this experimental data, the nuclear theory of the atom emerged. This theory proposes an atomic model rather like the solar system in miniature. At the center is a small, densely packed mass—the nucleus. At comparatively large distances from the nucleus are the various electrons in their orbits.

One serious objection to this theory remained. Classic physics could not explain how electrons could stay in their orbits and yet radiate energy. Niels Bohr solved this problem in 1913 when he applied quantum theory to energy radiation by electrons. According to Bohr's theory, electrons do not radiate energy constantly, but only in quanta (tiny packets) when they are excited. With this adjustment, the nuclear theory of the atom has gained widespread and enduring acceptance.

Rutherford was the first scientist to produce the disintegration of an atom artificially. He bombarded nitrogen atoms with alpha particles and produced oxygen atoms and hydrogen atoms (protons). This was the true beginning of the nuclear age. Rutherford's experiment profoundly influenced nuclear research of the 1920's and 1930's.

Rutherford also speculated on the existence of the neutron in the atomic nucleus. Sir James Chadwick, an associate of Rutherford at the Cavendish Laboratory, eventually discovered the neutron in 1932.

In later life, Rutherford established a reputation as an administrator, a mentor to students, and an advocate of science and scientists. From 1919 he served as Cavendish professor at Cambridge University. This position gave Rutherford a unique opportunity to guide and influence the direction of physics research. He served as president of the Royal Society in 1925-1930. When the Academic Assistance Council was set up to help student refugees from Germany, Rutherford served as its chairman.

Ernest Rutherford was born in New Zealand in 1871. He attended undergraduate school in New Zealand. As a student, he conducted experiments on electromagnetic waves—then a very new field. Rutherford's work attracted attention in England, and he won a scholarship to Cambridge. There he became associated with J. J. Thomson and the Cavendish Laboratory.

In 1898 Rutherford received an appointment as physics professor at McGill University in Montreal, Canada. He remained in Canada until 1907, when he returned to England to be professor of physics at Manchester University. Rutherford became Cavendish professor at Cambridge in 1919, succeeding his teacher and mentor, J. J. Thomson.

In addition to his science awards and honors, Rutherford received civic honors as well. He was made a knight in 1914. Then, in 1931, he was made a member of nobility—Baron Rutherford of Nelson.

Lord Rutherford died in 1937. He is buried in Westminster Abbey, a great honor for an English citizen.

Thomas Hunt Morgan

Thomas Hunt Morgan (1866-1945) was one of the greatest U.S. scientists and one of the most important geneticists of modern times. Morgan expanded the basic principles of heredity as described by Gregor Mendel and developed the modern science of genetics, the study of heredity.

Morgan's most famous work involved breeding generations of fruit flies. These flies have the scientific name *Drosophila melanogaster,* which is usually shortened to *Drosophila.* Like Gregor Mendel almost half a century before, Morgan identified particular traits, which he then traced through many generations. But Morgan was able to deepen our understanding of the ways in which heredity works.

Morgan proved that genes are the basic units that transmit particular traits. (He adopted the term *gene* from another scientist and popularized it.) Gregor Mendel had theorized about the action of genes, but was unable to prove his theories. Moreover, Morgan showed that genes are arranged in a linear fashion (that is, in a single line) on larger units called chromosomes.

Morgan and his research team at Columbia University in New York City conducted large-scale research on *Drosophila* during the years 1909-15. They made many important discoveries that advanced the science of genetics. Morgan found that some traits are sex-linked. The genes for these traits are located on the chromosomes that control the sex of the offspring. This discovery implied that only one sex of a species develops certain traits. In human beings, for instance, color-blindness usually affects men.

Morgan's research showed that genes, which are strung together on a chromosome, can be mapped. In other words, a particular gene may be linked to a specific location on a chromosome. By the 1980's, scientists had mapped hundreds of genes on human chromosomes. This information helps us in many ways. For instance, the gene that causes a particular illness can be pinpointed. Finding the gene for a disease opens new avenues of research that may eventually lead to treatment and a cure.

Morgan's genetic discoveries had a great impact on other areas of science as well. An understanding of how genes and chromosomes pass traits to new generations helped clarify some difficulties in Darwin's theory of natural selection (theory of evolution). Though this theory has never been proved, many scientists accept it. Also, genetic knowledge clarified many processes in the cell and opened the door to further research in cell chemistry.

Furthermore, Morgan strongly advocated an experimental approach to biology. For most of the 1800's, biology was dominated by morphology—the study of structure—rather than experimental research. Morgan's attitudes and his own scientific research helped change the outlook of a whole generation of biologists.

Morgan strongly influenced the study of biology in another important way. He helped establish two important marine laboratories—the Marine Biological Laboratory in Woods Hole, Massachusetts (1890's) and the Marine Laboratory of the California Institute of Technology at Corona del Mar (after 1928). Morgan believed that biologists in all fields would benefit from studying marine animals, because they are among the simpler, more primitive animals. Furthermore, Morgan established strong academic departments in genetics at both Columbia University and the California Institute of Technology. Future generations of biologists and geneticists would be influenced by Morgan.

Thomas Hunt Morgan was born in Kentucky in 1866. He studied at the State College (later university) of Kentucky and earned a Ph.D. at Johns Hopkins University. In the 1890's Morgan joined the faculty at Bryn Mawr College in Pennsylvania. In 1894-95 Morgan had the opportunity to work with the German embryologist, Hans Driesch. During and after this time, Morgan conducted research in embryology, the study of young organisms as they develop from fertilized eggs.

In 1904 Morgan joined the faculty of Columbia University as the professor of experimental zoology. (Zoology is the study of animals.) Over the next 24 years, Morgan conducted his most fundamental research in genetics. Also in 1904, Morgan married Lillian V. Sampson, a biologist. Lillian Sampson Morgan worked with her husband in genetics research. She did a great deal of original work on sex-linked inheritance in *Drosophila.*

In 1928 Morgan accepted the invitation to organize a division of biology at the California Institute of Technology. There Morgan and his

Thomas Hunt Morgan and his associates identify the gene as the basic unit of heredity and the chromosome as the cellular structure on which genes reside.

Paul Ehrlich introduces chemotherapy to the treatment of infectious diseases.

 1910

 1910

Marie Curie publishes a fundamental treatise on radioactivity.

Francis Peyton Rous proves that viruses cause certain types of cancer.

assistants continued research on chromosomes.

Morgan won many prizes and awards. In 1924 he received the Darwin Medal. He was awarded the Nobel Prize for medicine or physiology for his work with *Drosophila* in 1933. The Royal Society of London bestowed the coveted Copley Medal on Morgan in 1939. (Morgan was a foreign member of the Royal Society.)

Morgan was also active in many scientific associations. In addition to his Royal Society membership, Morgan served as president of the National Academy of Sciences, of the American Association for the Advancement of Science, and of the Sixth International Congress of Genetics.

Thomas Hunt Morgan died in 1945. His writings include a number of basic texts on genetics. In 1905 he co-authored *The Mechanism of Mendelian Heredity,* which showed how the new research on genes and chromosomes confirmed and extended Mendel's basic laws of heredity. In *The Theory of the Gene,* Morgan further described his experimental work in Mendelian terms. In *Experimental Zoology,* Morgan strongly advocated an experimental approach in the study of biology. Morgan applied his genetic theories to the study of embryology in *Embryology and Genetics* (1934). He also wrote books about Darwin's theory of evolution, including *A Critique of the Theory of Evolution* (1925). Morgan originally rejected Darwin's theory, but came to accept it as his own genetic research advanced. A prolific writer, Morgan authored a number of other books.

Paul Ehrlich

Paul Ehrlich (1854-1915) was a German medical researcher who made enormous contributions to our understanding of disease and to the development of treatments for disease. Ehrlich also developed drugs to combat several diseases.

Ehrlich conducted painstaking medical research in a variety of fields. Eventually, these researches led him to develop several strategies for combating disease organisms. One

strategy is known as *serum therapy.* This approach grew out of Ehrlich's study of immunity in human cells. Ehrlich believed that when cells are exposed to *toxins,* or poisons produced by one-celled organisms such as bacteria, the cells gradually develop immunity through complex chemical changes. The problem in infections is that the cells are overwhelmed by too much toxin before they can carry out the chemical changes required for immunity. Experimentally, Ehrlich was able to solve this problem by exposing rabbits to a toxin in gradually increased doses over time. Eventually, Ehrlich's rabbits were able to withstand a concentration of toxin 5,000 times greater than a normally fatal dose.

Around 1890, Ehrlich worked closely with Emil von Behring, who had developed an experimental antitoxin against diphtheria. *Antitoxin* is a substance that works against a toxin. At that time, diphtheria was a common childhood disease that often proved fatal. Ehrlich used live horses' blood to produce a diphtheria serum that could be used effectively and practically in humans.

Another disease-fighting therapy developed by Paul Ehrlich is *chemotherapy.* In chemotherapy, chemical substances are introduced in the human bloodstream to fight pathogens, agents (such as bacteria) that cause disease. The substances must be able to weaken or kill the pathogen without harming human tissue. Ehrlich turned to chemotherapy because he found that serum therapy was sometimes not effective.

Ehrlich's most acclaimed achievement was in the field of chemotherapy. He developed a safe, effective drug against syphilis, a devastating disease that had been widespread and untreatable for most of human history. Syphilis, caused by a tiny, one-celled organism, works slowly in the body but gradually produces terrible effects and brings about death. Ehrlich tested hundreds of chemicals against the syphilis pathogen. Substance number 606 worked very well without causing ill effects to the human body, even though it contained arsenic in its chemical make-up. Ehrlich's antisyphilis drug became known as "preparation 606." Later it was named Salvarsan. Ehrlich tested his drug in the most widespread clinical tests ever conducted up to that time. In the end, Salvarsan was widely recognized as a highly effective medical weapon, able to cure

Marie Curie receives the Nobel Prize in chemistry for her work in isolating radium.

 1911

Ernest Rutherford formulates the modern nuclear theory of the atom.

 1911

Heike Onnes discovers superconductivity.

a deadly disease. In fact, the nickname that Ehrlich himself coined, "the magic bullet," seemed appropriate.

Ehrlich made many other important contributions to biology and medicine. He developed an improved staining technique for the tuberculosis bacillus, the germ that causes tuberculosis. Usually, such microscopic organisms must be stained with a dye before they can be seen clearly under a microscope. Ehrlich's staining technique aided in the diagnosis of tuberculosis in human patients. Ehrlich also developed a method to stain blood cells.

Ehrlich developed research methods for studying cancer cells. He produced strains of cancer cells that are still used in experiments with anticancer drugs. Ehrlich also made valuable contributions to the treatment of eye diseases.

Ehrlich conducted studies of oxygen use in cells. These studies helped scientists understand some of the basic functions of living cells.

Paul Ehrlich was born in Prussia, an area now in East Germany and Poland, in 1854. He studied medicine at the University of Leipzig, Germany, where his research work attracted the attention of prominent German medical researchers. Ehrlich accepted an invitation to do research at the Charité Hospital in Berlin, at that time a great medical research center.

As a fairly young man, Ehrlich became ill with tuberculosis. He went to Egypt to seek a cure. In 1889 he returned to Berlin, his tuberculosis permanently arrested. Ehrlich went to work at Robert Koch's Institute for Infectious Diseases, where he began his work on serum therapy. In the 1890's he was made director of a research institute that was later named the Royal Institute for Experimental Therapy and moved to Frankfort am Main, a small city in southwestern Germany. The research emphasis at the Royal Institute suited Ehrlich well, and he conducted many of his most important studies there.

For his great achievement in finding a syphilis cure, Paul Ehrlich gained worldwide fame. Ehrlich shared the 1908 Nobel Prize for physiology or medicine with Russian biologist Élie Metchnikoff. This honor was awarded Ehrlich for his work in serum therapy. The German government granted Ehrlich honors, such as the title Privy Councillor. A number of universities, including those of Oxford, Chicago, and Athens, bestowed honorary doctoral degrees on Ehrlich. Paul Ehrlich died of strokes in August, 1915.

Niels Bohr

Niels Bohr (1885-1962), a Danish physicist, was one of the greatest and most influential scientists of the twentieth century. Bohr developed basic ideas about the structure of an atom. These ideas have been widely accepted by scientists ever since. Bohr's work contributed strongly to most of the important discoveries in physics during and since his lifetime. For his important work, Bohr was awarded the Nobel Prize in physics in 1922.

Bohr, along with other distinguished physicists of the early 1900's, developed a new branch of physics known as *quantum mechanics.* These physicists recognized that the laws of motion and gravity formulated by Sir Isaac Newton in the 1600's (called the Newtonian laws) could not properly explain motion at the atomic level. Newton had developed his physics with the movements of planets in mind. Early atomic researchers—scientists such as Ernest Rutherford and J. J. Thomson—had thought of atoms as tiny models of the solar system. The nucleus was rather like the sun and the electrons were like planets whirring about the sun. As physicists probed deeper into the atom, however, they gradually realized that the solar system is not an accurate model for atomic motion.

Albert Einstein, Max Planck, Niels Bohr, and others developed the theories of quantum mechanics in the early 1900's to better describe the atom and its motion. Several important ideas emerged. One is that radiation—such as light—is emitted in a stream of separate bundles of energy called *quanta.* This principle can also be applied to atomic radiation, such as that of electrons. These speculations led physicists to conclude that atomic particles, such as electrons, have properties of *both* particles and waves. This idea came to be known as the "wave-particle duality" principle. It revolutionized physics. No longer could scientists calculate with certainty the position of an electron in its orbit at a particular moment. Such

Alfred Wegener proposes the continental drift theory.

 1912

1913

Robert Millikan measures the charge of the electron.

movements, according to quantum mechanics, can be mathematically described only as probabilities. In other words, since a particle, such as an electron, has qualities of both a particle and a wave, the traditional Newtonian laws of bodies in motion do not apply to it.

Niels Bohr developed these ideas further. He claimed that an atom exists in a series of stable states. Between such states, a jump in energy level—a "quantum jump"—occurs in the atom. The jump can be to a higher energy level (increase) or to a lower energy level (decrease). Such a change in energy happens in a fraction of time. With every quantum jump, light photons are given off. Photons are quanta—tiny bundles—of light energy. Bohr based this theory on observations of the spectrum of light that the element hydrogen gives off. Every chemical element gives off a unique spectrum—that is, band of light frequencies. Bohr thought that the band of light frequencies given off by a chemical element could only be explained by the theory of "quantum jumps" of energy in the atom. Scientific observations made during and after his lifetime have proved his theory true.

Bohr devoted most of his scientific career to development of a quantum theory that would be complete enough to explain all of the motions of the atom. He also applied quantum theories to many of the chemical elements. He worked to find reasons in quantum mechanics for the regular patterns that occur in the periodic table of elements.

Niels Bohr strongly influenced the physicists and scientists of his time. The reasons for this influence went beyond Bohr's own contributions to physics. In 1921 the University of Copenhagen opened a new Institute of Theoretic Physics with Niels Bohr as its director. This institute became the world center for exchange of ideas among physicists. The institute owed much of its success and influence to its director. Bohr was a scientist who welcomed the exchange of ideas. He also formed close friendships with his co-workers and encouraged them in their work. In his own country as well as abroad, Niels Bohr earned the respect of fellow scientists. He served as president of the Royal Danish Academy from 1939 until his death in 1962.

Bohr appreciated friendly disagreements in science. He was always willing to listen to the opposing view on a topic. A famous debate developed between Bohr and Albert Einstein.

This argument centered on the philosophical conclusions that might be drawn from quantum physics. The new physics introduced uncertainties into mathematical description of atomic movements. One uncertainty is that of the motion of electrons, since they have properties of both particles and waves. Furthermore, quantum physicists concluded that they could not be sure of their own measurements. Such measurements are based on the scattering of light. But the very action of showering atomic particles with light photons, which bounce off and scatter, causes the particles themselves to move. Such movement cannot be predicted mathematically. Bohr felt that these uncertainties indicated permanent, radical changes in the study of physics. Einstein, on the other hand, believed that future discoveries and perhaps better scientific instruments would do away with the uncertainties. Einstein and Bohr never agreed on this topic, but their argument remained friendly. In today's physics, Bohr's position seems more correct. No discoveries or new techniques have yet explained away the uncertainties introduced by quantum mechanics. On the other hand, physicists cannot be sure what discoveries the future will bring in quantum mechanics.

Niels Bohr was born in Copenhagen, Denmark, in 1885. His father was a famous professor at the University of Copenhagen. His mother was from a family that had been important in banking and in government. The Bohr children were encouraged to excel in their studies. Niels's brother, Harald, became a brilliant mathematician.

Niels attended the University of Copenhagen, where he won a gold medal from the Royal Danish Academy of Sciences and Letters for original scientific research. In 1911 he went to England to study with the great physicist Sir J. J. Thomson at Cambridge University. The next year he went to the University of Manchester, where he studied with Ernest Rutherford. At this time, Rutherford was developing his nuclear model of the atom. Rutherford's ideas profoundly affected Bohr and led to the younger man's own landmark theories. In 1912 Bohr returned to Copenhagen. Eventually he became a professor at the University of Copenhagen and director of the Institute of Theoretical Physics. Because Denmark remained neutral in World War I, Bohr was able to continue his work throughout the years of the war.

During the 1920's and 1930's, Bohr ex-

Niels Bohr, the Danish physicist, developed basic ideas about the structure of the atom

Niels Bohr publishes his theory of atomic structure.

1914

changed ideas with most of the physicists of the time and traveled widely. This creative and satisfying period came to an abrupt end in 1940 when Nazi Germany invaded and occupied Denmark. Bohr attempted to continue his work. By 1943, however, his anti-Nazi views and Jewish ancestry on his mother's side caused great dangers for Bohr and his family. In that year, Bohr and his family escaped to Sweden in a fishing boat. Later Bohr and his son went to England, where they worked on projects to develop a nuclear fission bomb. This research eventually led the Bohrs, father and son, to the Los Alamos, New Mexico, laboratory that made the first practical atomic bomb in 1945.

Meanwhile, Bohr had become deeply worried about the dangers of the atomic weapon upon which he was working. He talked to both President Roosevelt and Prime Minister Churchill about the need for international atomic cooperation. Later he urged the United Nations to encourage such a policy.

Bohr also promoted such postwar international efforts as the First International Conference on the Peaceful Uses of Atomic Energy (Geneva, Switzerland, 1955). He also helped create the European Council for Nuclear Research (CERN). For these efforts, Niels Bohr received the first U.S. Atoms for Peace Award in 1957. When Bohr died in 1962 he was widely recognized as one of the greatest scientists, public figures, and peace advocates of his time.

Ernest Everett Just

Ernest Everett Just (1883-1941) was an American biologist who conducted studies of living cells and how they function. He also did research on the reproductive processes of certain sea animals. For his work, Just won the Spingarn Medal in 1915. This award is given each year to a black who has excelled in his or her field.

Just studied fertilization in marine invertebrates, sea animals without backbones. This work led him to investigate the role of the cell surface in such animals. Just's research led him to conclude that all parts of the cell influence the cell's activities. This was a radical idea, be-

cause most biologists believed that the nucleus controlled all of the cell's activities.

Ernest Everett Just was born in Charleston, South Carolina, in 1883. He received a bachelor's degree from Dartmouth College in 1907 and began teaching at Howard University the same year. He received a doctor's degree from the University of Chicago in 1916. From 1909 through 1930, Just spent most summers conducting research at the Marine Biological Laboratory in Woods Hole, Massachusetts. This is a prestigious laboratory where many important marine biologists, including Rachel Carson, have worked.

During the last decade of his life, Just worked mostly in European laboratories. He wanted to escape the racial discrimination that existed then in the United States. No civil rights bills had been passed in the United States since the time immediately after the Civil War. Until the 1960's and later, black Americans had difficulty being accepted in many professions.

Ernest Everett Just published accounts of his research and his conclusions in two books. The books are *The Biology of the Cell Surface* and *Basic Methods for Experiments on Eggs of Marine Animals.* Just died in 1941.

George Washington Carver

George Washington Carver (1864-1943) was an American agricultural scientist. Through scientific research, Carver discovered hundreds of ways to use a number of crops that grow well in the soils of the southern United States. His work helped change the economy of the rural South and encouraged industrial growth. Carver also promoted agricultural training and education in the United States.

Southern agriculture was in a terrible condition when Carver began his work at Tuskegee Institute in Alabama in the 1890's. Years of cotton cultivation had worn out the soils. The southern economy, dependent on a single cash crop, was shaky. Carver saw that new crops were needed to enrich the soil and to reduce Southern dependence on cotton. He identified several common crops that grow well in the South—peanuts, soybeans, and sweet potatoes. These crops were not taken seriously as income-earners, but Carver

George Washington Carver develops an enormous variety of industrial uses for American agricultural crops.

Gilbert Lewis describes electron bonding between atoms.

Ernest Rutherford produces the first artificial disintegration of an atom.

| 1915 | ca. 1916 | 1916 | 1919 |

Ernest Everett Just receives the Springarn Medal for his study of fertilization in marine invertebrates and the role of the cell surface in the development of such organisms.

Albert Einstein publishes his general theory of relativity.

thought they might yield new, useful products. Moreover, peanuts and soybeans actually return nutrients to the soil.

Carver experimented with these plants in his laboratory. In time, he found many new uses for them.

Carver showed how to make 300 different products from peanuts. A few of these are milk, cheese, flour, ink, wood stain, linoleum, and cosmetics. The list of products for sweet potatoes includes vinegar, rubber, ink, glue, and about 100 more items. Carver made similar discoveries with the soybean.

Carver also experimented with hybrids, plants that are offspring of parent plants with differing characteristics. For instance, he developed a hybrid form of cotton that was better than varieties often raised in the South. He also developed plants that produced very large vegetables.

With the help of the Tuskegee Institute, Carver spread agricultural information across the rural South. He ran a "school on wheels," traveling to various rural districts to communicate his ideas for improving agriculture. He also published an agricultural journal from Tuskegee. In 1921 Carver appeared before a Congressional committee to publicize the uses he had found for peanuts. Carver was so dedicated to agricultural education and research, that he willed his life savings to an agricultural research foundation at the Tuskegee Institute.

George Washington Carver was born a slave in Missouri before the end of the Civil War and emancipation. His owner was named Moses Carver, from whom the young boy took his last name. Until he reached the age of 10 or 12, young George remained with the Moses Carver family. Afterward, he roamed through Missouri and Kansas, doing odd jobs, and get-

A photograph of **George Washington Carver** in his research greenhouse at the Tuskegee Institute

Louis de Broglie proposes the wave theory of the electron.

Thomas Hunt Morgan publishes *The Theory of the Gene,* a landmark study of genetics.

1921   1924   1925   1926

John James Macleod and **Sir Frederick Banting** discover insulin.

Erwin Schrodinger develops the principles of wave mechanics.

ting a basic education on his own. Carver managed to get a high school education by the time he was in his 20's. After being turned down for admission by a college in Kansas, Carver was accepted by Simpson College in Iowa. Later he went to Iowa State Agricultural College. In 1896 he was awarded a master of science degree.

After graduation, Carver obtained a teaching position at Tuskegee Institute, a black agricultural and industrial college in Alabama. The great educator, Booker T. Washington, was director of Tuskegee at that time.

Carver taught classes and conducted agricultural research at Tuskegee. After 1910, he was allowed to devote all his time to research. Carver remained at Tuskegee until his death in 1943.

In later life, George Washington Carver became a world celebrity. He had the opportunity to meet such figures as Henry Ford, Mahatma Ghandi, and Henry Wallace, cabinet member and vice president under Franklin Roosevelt. Carver was personally visited by at least two presidents—Calvin Coolidge and Franklin Roosevelt. Joseph Stalin, the dictator of the Soviet Union, also knew about Carver's work. Stalin invited Carver to come to the Soviet Union to help with cotton cultivation there. Carver refused the invitation.

As he became widely known and admired, many awards and honors came to Carver. The London Royal Society for the Encouragement of Arts, Manufactures, and Commerce elected him as a fellow in 1916. In 1923 Carver won the Spingarn Medal, an award for black achievement. Carver also won the Roosevelt Medal in 1939 and the Thomas A. Edison Foundation Award in 1942.

Even after his death, Carver has been honored in many ways. Congress has designated January 5 as a day to honor Carver annually. A George Washington Carver National Monument has been established at the site of the Moses Carver farm in Missouri. Tuskegee University in Alabama maintains a George Washington Carver Museum. In 1973, George Washington Carver was elected to the Hall of Fame for Great Americans.

Hermann Joseph Muller

Hermann Joseph Muller (1890-1967) was one of the founders of the modern science of genetics. Muller won the 1946 Nobel Prize for physiology or medicine for demonstrating that X rays cause mutations in genes. A mutation is a sudden change in the structure of the DNA molecules that pass genetic information from one generation to the next.

Muller performed genetic experiments on *Drosophila,* the fruit fly originally selected by Thomas Hunt Morgan for genetic studies. Muller had worked with Morgan's research teams for several years at Columbia University. In the 1920's, Muller performed genetic experiments to determine the effects of X rays on *Drosophila.* He found that X rays can cause mutations in individual genes as well as breakage of chromosomes. Chromosomes are the cellular structures on which genes are located.

Muller's discovery greatly advanced the science of genetics. Biologists now had a way to cause genetic mutations in experimental animals, such as *Drosophila.* This capability helped them study many cellular processes at the molecular level.

Muller also studied the effects of X-ray mutations on organisms. He found that a large majority of such mutations are harmful. Only a very few introduce changes that help an organism. These studies helped explain some questions that Charles Darwin had not been able to answer in his theory of evolution by natural selection. If mutations can occur suddenly and randomly and if most are harmful, then the process of natural selection eventually selects beneficial mutations over harmful ones.

Muller believed that his studies of mutations pointed out the dangers of radiation to human beings. With the development of the atomic bomb in the 1940's, Muller became a powerful spokesperson for the need to control such weapons. He believed that the radiation released in nuclear warfare would harm countless future generations of humans through genetic mutations.

Muller wrote a classic scientific paper on "The Mechanism of Crossing Over" while still a graduate student at Columbia. During cell division in which a gamete (sex cell) is formed, the paired chromosomes prepare to separate. Genes are lined up in long chains on the chromosomes. Some genes are independent,

Hermann Joseph Muller
publishes his discovery
that X rays can cause
genetic mutation.

 1927

1928

Sir Alexander Fleming
discovers penicillin.

while others are linked together in linkage groups. Linkage groups on paired chromosomes often exchange places on their respective chromosomes before the chromosomes separate. This process is called "crossing over."

Hermann Joseph Muller was born in New York City in 1890. He went to Columbia University in 1907 on scholarship. In 1912 he became a lab assistant on Thomas Hunt Morgan's research team at Columbia. This group confirmed and expanded the laws of heredity originally proposed by Gregor Mendel in the 1860's. Morgan's team identified genes as the basic unit of heredity and showed how genes are positioned on chromosomes. Much of their work is summarized in *The Mechanism of Mendelian Heredity,* published in 1915.

In 1920 Muller accepted a position as professor of zoology at the University of Texas, Austin. While there during the 1920's, Muller performed most of his work on X-ray mutations.

In 1932-1933, Muller spent a year at the Kaiser Wilhelm Institute in Berlin. From there, Muller went to Leningrad and Moscow in the Soviet Union. Politically a socialist, Muller at first approved of Stalin's government. During his stay in the Soviet Union, however, Muller became entangled in a genetic controversy then raging. Stalin's government backed the genetic theories of Trofim Denisovich Lysenko. Lysenko's ideas were unsupported and antiscientific. In time, Lysenkoism was proven completely false. For over 20 years, however, the Soviet government held strongly to Lysenko's thought. (Lysenko remained a powerful figure in Soviet politics until after the fall of Khrushchev in 1964; he died in 1976.) In the 1930's, however, opposition to Lysenko and his system of genetics became politically dangerous. Muller tried to oppose Lysenko, but eventually he had to leave the Soviet Union.

Muller then took up a position at the Institute of Animal Genetics in Edinburgh, Scotland. He made a strong impact on the science of genetics in Great Britain.

Muller returned to the United States in 1940. He enjoyed a distinguished career as professor of zoology at Indiana University from 1945 to 1964. During this period, Muller won his Nobel Prize (1946). Hermann Joseph Muller died in 1967.

Sir Alexander Fleming

Sir Alexander Fleming (1881-1955), a Scottish bacteriologist, discovered, in 1928, the germ-killing power of penicillin, a substance made by a green mold. This discovery led eventually to the age of antibiotics in medicine. Antibiotics are substances produced by one type of organism (such as molds) that are capable of weakening or destroying germs. Many diseases that were once life threatening to humans and animals are now easily cured by antibiotics. Also, the risk of infection in surgery or following injury is much lower today than before antibiotics were available.

Fleming was working as a researcher and lecturer at St. Mary's Hospital, University of London, when he made his discovery. He had prepared cultures of *Staphylococcus,* disease-causing bacteria, for routine experiments. A germ culture is made by putting a germ-free gel in a special glass dish and adding some cells of the germ organism, such as bacteria. Also nutrients, or food for the germs, must be added. Fleming noticed that one of his bacteria cultures had become contaminated with a mold. Normally, a researcher would want a

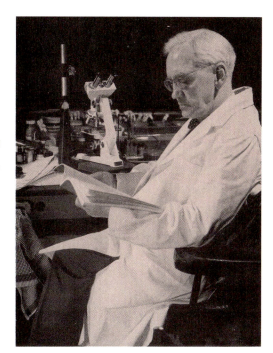

Sir Alexander Fleming, Scottish bacteriologist, photographed in 1954 in his laboratory at the Wright-Fleming Institute

Charles Elton, an English biologist, publishes *Animal Ecology and Evolution,* a landmark study of the balance of nature.

Clyde Tombaugh discovers the planet Pluto.

1927   **1929**   **1930**

Edwin Hubble demonstrates that the universe is expanding.

Karl Landsteiner wins the Nobel Prize in physiology or medicine for his identification of human blood types.

germ culture to remain free of other organisms, so that it may be studied more easily. Fleming's mistake, however, led to a great discovery. All around the mold was a ring of clear gel separating the mold from bacteria in the rest of the dish. This could only mean that the mold was giving off a substance that killed the bacteria. Fleming realized the importance of what he saw.

Fleming conducted a careful investigation of the *Penicillium* mold. He extracted the powerful germ-killing substance from the mold and named it *penicillin.* Tests showed that penicillin could kill germs even when diluted or weakened by adding another substance, such as water, 800 times. Fleming made penicillin known to the world in 1929, publishing his findings in the *British Journal of Experimental Pathology.*

Fleming's discovery, however, was only the first step in a long journey that would lead to antibiotic drugs. For about a decade, little work was done on penicillin. Then in 1939, two British researchers, Howard Florey and Ernst Chain, led a research team in tests on penicillin. The Florey-Chain group found a way to isolate and purify penicillin from its mold. This had been the major stumbling block in developing a useful drug from the substance. The first test of penicillin on a human being came in 1941. A British policeman who was critically ill from blood poisoning was given the drug. However, he died because the supply of penicillin was inadequate to kill the infectious bacteria.

By about 1945, the Florey-Chain research team had found a way to produce penicillin in large amounts. For their work with penicillin, Fleming, Florey, and Chain shared the 1945 Nobel Prize for physiology or medicine.

Although Sir Alexander Fleming is most remembered for penicillin, he conducted other important research as well. For instance, he identified lysozome, a germ-killing substance in tears and saliva, in 1921. He isolated the substance and conducted experiments to test its power against germs.

Alexander Fleming was born in Scotland. He studied bacteriology at St. Mary's Hospital Medical School, London University. This is the medical facility where Fleming also spent most of his professional life. During World War I, Fleming served with distinction in the Royal Army Medical Corps. He was elected to the Royal Society in 1943 and was made a knight in 1944.

Charles Elton

Charles Elton (1900-   ), an English biologist, did pioneering studies in the field of ecology and helped establish ecology as a science. Ecology is the study of the relationships of living things to their environment and to each other. In the years since World War II, it has been recognized as one of the most important areas of study and research. Modern societies are changing the surface of the earth at a rapid rate. Two factors—rapid population growth and advancing technology—are behind these changes. Some of the changes threaten the well-being of particular organisms, and some threaten all life on earth. Ecologists can draw our attention to these trends as they develop and suggest ways to change them.

Charles Elton devoted his professional life to the study of animal ecology. He began with the work of traditional naturalists—observers of the natural world, especially plants and animals—and went on to formulate the basic principles of modern ecology. These principles have been widely accepted as basic factors in studying the ecology of an area.

Elton studied the requirements of particular animals and plants for food. This led him to develop the concept of the *ecological niche,* the idea that each species has a unique function and place within the environment. Elton also studied the interconnections in the food needs of plants and animals in an environment. He measured the amount of plant food required to produce a given amount of animal tissue in an animal that feeds on the plants. Then he measured the amount of animal meat required to produce a given amount of body tissue in the animal that eats the first animal. So he continued up the food chain, until he reached the highest animal in the chain. Elton called this natural system the *pyramid of food relations.* The startling conclusion of these studies is that an enormous amount of plant material at the bottom of the chain is required to produce a relatively small amount of animal tissue at the top of the chain.

Elton also studied animal populations. From the Hudson Bay Company he was able to obtain records of fur-bearing mammals in regions of Canada dating back to 1736. This valuable data allowed Elton to observe animal populations over a long period of time. Using the techniques gained in this work, Elton conducted studies of the mouse and vole population in England. (Voles are small, mouselike ro-

Sir James Chadwick discovers the atomic neutron.

1931

1932

Karl Jansky detects radio waves outside the solar system.

dents.) During World War II, Elton applied these studies to rodent control, thereby protecting and conserving the British food supply during wartime.

In the postwar period, Elton studied habitats. A *habitat* is the particular type of environment an organism needs to live. For instance, deep-sea fishes need a saltwater, ocean environment. Cactus plants need a desertlike environment. And polar bears require a cold Arctic habitat. A related area of study is that of the community—an area that serves as the habitat for many plants and animals together. Elton explored these relationships in his work.

Charles Elton was born at Manchester, England, in 1900. He began his college studies at Liverpool College, then went on to Oxford University, where he studied zoology. While still an undergraduate, Elton assisted Julian Huxley, a famous biologist, on a biological expedition. This expedition gave Elton the opportunity to conduct ecological studies in a remote natural environment.

Elton published his first book, *Animal Ecology,* a landmark study of animal communities, in 1927. In 1930 Elton published a controversial book, *Animal Ecology and Evolution,* in which he questioned traditional ideas about the so-called "balance of nature" as it applies to animal populations. In 1932 Elton opened the Bureau of Animal Population at Oxford University. This facility became a world center for information about animal ecology. Elton became editor of a new scientific journal for ecology, the *Journal of Animal Ecology,* in 1932.

Elton wrote other books, many of them important in the development of ecology as a science. In 1942 he published his study on *Voles, Mice, and Lemmings. The Control of Rats and Mice* appeared in 1954. It described the war work of Elton and his co-workers in protecting the food supply from rodents. *The Ecology of Invasions of Animals and Plants* was published in 1958 and *The Pattern of Animal Communities* in 1966.

Charles Elton has been honored in many ways. He was elected a fellow of the Royal Society of London in 1953. He was also made a foreign member of the American Academy of Arts and Sciences. In 1967 he received the Gold Medal of the Linnean Society. The Royal Society's Darwin Medal was awarded him in 1970. Elton retired in 1967.

Sir James Chadwick

Sir James Chadwick (1891-1974) was a British physicist who discovered the atomic neutron, winning the 1935 Nobel Prize for physics for this work.

Beginning in 1923, Chadwick worked with Ernest Rutherford at Cambridge University's Cavendish Laboratory. These two physicists and their assistants conducted experimental investigation of the atom, particularly the particles that make up the nucleus of an atom. They identified the proton, or positively-charged particle, of the hydrogen atom as a component of every atomic nucleus.

In 1932 Chadwick observed curious results when he bombarded the element beryllium with alpha particles. The beryllium emitted an unknown radiation, which then dislodged protons from the nuclei of other atoms. Chadwick concluded that the mysterious radiation consisted of particles having a mass equal to a proton but carrying no electrical charge. Had the particle carried a charge, he reasoned, its movement would have been affected by other charged particles. In fact, the particle had directly penetrated the atomic nucleus. Chadwick named the newly discovered particle the *neutron,* meaning a particle with no charge.

Chadwick's discovery provided an important tool for further experimentation with the atomic nucleus. The neutron, because it carries no charge, could be used to penetrate the atomic nucleus. It would be used in experiments later in the 1930's to break up the atomic nucleus.

Sir James Chadwick was born near Manchester, England. He studied at the Universities of Manchester, Cambridge, and Berlin. In 1945 he was made a knight.

Enrico Fermi

Enrico Fermi (1901-1954) was an Italian-born, Americanized physicist who made fundamental contributions to modern nuclear physics. Fermi was the first scientist to split the atom, although he did not realize what he had done at the time. Later, Fermi and his co-workers developed the first atomic weapon, which was eventually used in warfare against Japan in 1945.

Otto Hahn and **Fritz Strassman** split the uranium atom, and **Lise Meitner** and **Otto Frisch** develop a mathematical theory to explain the split.

1934

1938-1939

Enrico Fermi splits the atom.

In 1934 Frédéric and Irène Joliot-Curie produced artificial radioactivity by bombarding elements with alpha particles. Fermi wanted to build on this experimental work. He used slowed-down neutrons obtained from radioactive beryllium, a chemical element, to bombard elements. This proved a very effective method to release radioactive particles from the bombarded material. When Fermi used uranium of atomic weight 92 as the target, however, he obtained unexpected radioactive substances. Fermi's co-workers thought the new substances might be a new element of atomic weight 93. Fermi did not claim to understand what had happened in the experiment when he reported its results.

Only years later did Fermi—and the world—realize that he had in fact crossed a great threshold in history. He had been the first person to split an atom in a way that could be controlled to harness atomic energy. (This process would later be called *nuclear fission.*) Fermi's experiment would lead to the development of the atomic bomb and nuclear energy.

The importance of Fermi's discovery was confirmed by three German scientists, Otto Hahn, Lise Meitner, and Fritz Strassmann, in 1938. Lise Meitner secretly went to Stockholm where, with her nephew, Otto Frisch, she announced the Hahn group's experimental conclusions to the world in January, 1939. She explained that they had split the uranium atom into the elements barium, krypton, and small amounts of other materials. According to Einstein's famous mass-energy equation, $E = mc^2$, nuclear fission, or splitting of the atom, could be expected to yield enormous amounts of energy.

In the meantime, Enrico Fermi had gone to Stockholm in 1938 to accept the Nobel Prize in physics. Fermi and his family used this opportunity to escape from Fascist Italy, settling in the United States. In New York, Fermi heard about the conclusions of the Hahn-Meitner-Strassman research team. The experiments were repeated at Columbia University with similar results and conclusions. Based on these experiments, Danish physicist Niels Bohr suggested the possibility of a nuclear chain reaction. Other physicists considered this suggestion and settled on uranium-235 as the best candidate for such a reaction.

Meanwhile, Fermi and two other scientists, Leo Szilard and Eugene Wigner, became concerned about the possibility that Hitler's scientists in Nazi Germany might achieve a chain reaction and develop an atomic weapon. This group drafted a letter to President Roosevelt. Albert Einstein signed the letter and presented it to the president on October 11, 1939. Out of this event developed the Manhattan Project, code name for a scientific team assembled in 1942 to develop an atomic bomb for the United States.

Fermi was chosen to produce a nuclear chain reaction in uranium-235. He developed an atomic pile, or nuclear reactor, to produce the controlled, self-sustaining chain reaction required. On December 2, 1942, Fermi and his team produced the first such chain reaction. This event led to the successful testing of the first atomic weapon on July 16, 1945, then to the atomic bombing of Hiroshima and Nagasaki in August, 1945.

Enrico Fermi was born in Rome. By the age of 21, he had earned his doctorate from the University of Pisa. He then did graduate work under the physicist Max Born, who profoundly influenced his scientific development, at the German University of Göttingen. Afterward, he returned to the University of Florence, then to the University of Rome, where he became a full professor in theoretical physics. In 1929 the Royal Academy of Italy elected Enrico Fermi to membership, the youngest member in its ranks.

In addition to the Nobel Prize, Fermi received the Congressional Medal of Merit in 1946. Two years earlier, the Fermis had become U.S. citizens. The Royal Society of London elected Fermi as a foreign member in 1950. The Enrico Fermi Award was established in his honor, and Fermi became its first recipient in 1954. An artificially produced chemical element, fermium, was named for him in 1952. Also, the Fermi National Accelerator Laboratory, a physics research laboratory near Chicago, bears his name.

Helen Sawyer Hogg publishes her *Catalogue of Variable Stars in Globular Clusters.*

Helen Brooke Taussig and **Alfred Blalock** team up to develop an operation to help blue babies.

1939   1940   1941   1942

Karl Landsteiner and **A. S. Wiener** discover the Rh factor in human blood.

Enrico Fermi produces the first controlled nuclear chain reaction.

Helen Sawyer Hogg

Helen Sawyer Hogg (1905-   ) is an American-born Canadian astronomer whose work has contributed significantly to our knowledge about variable stars. Also, Hogg is the first woman to have served as president of the Royal Astronomical Society of Canada. She accepted this position in 1957.

During her career, Helen Hogg has discovered more than 250 variable stars. These are stars whose light periodically varies in brightness. Most of the variable stars discovered by Hogg are in globular star clusters—ball-like star groups in the Milky Way galaxy. Hogg also determined the period of many variable stars. A variable star's period is the time its light takes to change from bright to dim and back to bright again. This information helps astronomers calculate how far the star is from earth.

Helen Hogg was born Helen Sawyer in Lowell, Mass. She married Frank S. Hogg, a Canadian astronomer, in 1930. Helen Hogg received her Ph.D. in astronomy in 1931. Later, in 1935, she joined the faculty of the University of Toronto in Canada. There she conducted most of her research. Her major work on variable stars, *Catalogue of Variable Stars in Globular Clusters,* was first published in 1939.

Helen Brooke Taussig

Helen Brooke Taussig (1898-1986), an American physician, was the codeveloper of the operation to correct the "blue baby" syndrome caused by a congenital heart defect. The operation has made it possible for thousands of children, otherwise doomed to an early death, to survive to reach maturity and lead productive lives.

A blue baby is an infant whose skin has a bluish tint owing to a lack of sufficient oxygen in the blood. Normally, blood containing carbon dioxide returns from the body to the heart, which sends it to the lungs, where oxygen replaces the carbon dioxide. Oxygenated blood then goes back to the heart to be circulated throughout the body. But certain kinds of heart defect, especially blockage or narrowing of the pulmonary artery and an opening between the ventricles of the heart, cause the

Dr. Helen Brooke Taussig visits with two young patients at Johns Hopkins. She helped develop an operation for blue babies.

heart to pump some unoxygenated blood. Consequently, the baby will appear blue and be often short of breath.

Dr. Taussig's work with young rheumatic fever patients at the Johns Hopkins Hospital in Baltimore in the 1930's led to her interest in blue babies. Her studies convinced her that an operation to rearrange blood passages in order to overcome the defect was possible.

In 1941, Dr. Taussig teamed up with Dr. Alfred Blalock, a pioneer heart surgeon, to develop the surgical technique to help blue babies. One way was to use one of the subclavian arteries, which lead to the arms, as a bypass for blood to flow from heart to lungs where it would receive enough oxygen.

In 1944, Dr. Blalock performed the first blue baby operation. By 1948, he had conducted the operation more than 100 times. This work encouraged surgeons to try even more complete repairs of heart defects. But the Blalock-Taussig operation still helps thousands of patients each year.

Dr. Taussig left Johns Hopkins Hospital temporarily in 1962 for Europe to investigate a sudden occurrence of malformed babies, many born without limbs. She traced the cause to a sleeping pill named thalidomide, which the mothers of these infants had taken during pregnancy. Her campaign to educate Americans and government agencies about the drug was in large part responsible for its being banned from sale in the United States.

Helen Brooke Taussig was born in Cambridge, Massachusetts. She received her M.D.

Oswald Avery demonstrates that genes consist of DNA.

 1943   **1944**

Selman Waksman discovers streptomycin.

Alfred Blalock performs the first blue baby operation.

degree from the Johns Hopkins University of Medicine in 1927. She received America's highest civilian award, the Presidential Medal of Freedom, and medical awards and honorary degrees from colleges and universities in the United States and abroad. She retired from Johns Hopkins in 1963 and and in 1965 became the first woman elected president of the American Heart Association.

Melvin Calvin

Melvin Calvin (1911-   ), an American biochemist, received the 1961 Nobel Prize for chemistry for his work in tracing the chain of chemical reactions involved in photosynthesis. In photosynthesis, green plants use the sun's energy to change water and carbon dioxide into sugar. Photosynthesis is of supreme importance to all living things. All food originally comes from photosynthesis.

Melvin Calvin began his experiments on photosynthesis in the mid-1940's. He caused a green alga called *Chlorella* to take in carbon-14, a radioactive substance. Then he stopped the alga's growth at different stages, analyzing the organism's use of carbon-14 at each stage. Over a period of time and after many experiments, Calvin was able to identify most of the chemical reactions that occur in photosynthesis.

Calvin was born in St. Paul, Minnesota. He received his Ph.D. from the University of Minnesota in 1935. Afterward he spent two years in England at the University of Manchester as a fellow of the Rockefeller Foundation. In 1946 he joined the faculty of the University of California at Berkeley, where he spent most of his career.

John Bardeen

John Bardeen (1908-   ), an American physicist, is the first person to win the Nobel Prize twice for work in the same field. Bardeen shared the 1956 Nobel Prize in physics with William Shockley and Walter Brattain for their work with semiconductors and the transistor

effect. He won the 1972 Nobel Prize in physics jointly with Leon Cooper and John Schrieffer for formulating a theory to explain superconductivity.

In 1947, Bardeen and his co-workers at Bell Laboratories invented the point-contact transistor. A transistor is a solid-state device that can function as an on-off switch or as an amplifier. A solid-state device is one that has no moving parts. The transistor made possible the rapid development of computers in the 1950's, the 1960's, and afterward. Before the transistor became commercially available in the 1950's, the computer had depended on vacuum tubes to perform switching tasks. Vacuum tubes were large, expensive, and not very reliable.

Invention of other types of transistors followed in the period 1947-1962. The transistors became smaller and more efficient. By the later 1960's, engineers were able to design integrated circuits, solid-state digital circuits that contain hundreds, thousands, or even millions of electronic components such as transistors. By the 1970's, such circuitry could be etched on a silicon chip small enough to fit in the eye of a needle.

During the 1950's, Bardeen worked with Cooper and Schrieffer on superconductivity. Many metals and certain other substances become superconductors when cooled to extremely cold temperatures. A superconductor conducts electricity with no measurable resistance. Bardeen and his co-workers developed a scientific theory to explain superconductivity. In 1957 they published this theory in an article in *The Physical Review.* For their work, the three researches shared the 1972 Nobel Prize.

The theoretical work of Bardeen, Cooper, and Schrieffer paved the way for intensive research into superconductors. By the mid-1980's, scientific research teams throughout the world were producing substances that become superconductive at relatively high temperatures. This work holds the promise of advances in many areas of science and technology in the very near future.

John Bardeen was born in Madison, Wisconsin, in 1908. He received a degree in electrical engineering from the University of Wisconsin in 1928. Later he received a Ph.D. from Princeton. Bardeen taught physics at the University of Minnesota and then worked for the U.S. Naval Ordnance Laboratory during World War II. In 1945 he went to work at Bell Laboratories, where with Brattain and Shockley, he

John Bardeen, Walter Brattain, and **William Shockley** invent the transistor.

ca. 1946   1947   ca. 1948

Melvin Calvin traces the chain of chemical reactions involved in photosynthesis.

John Franklin Enders and co-workers develop the means to grow the poliovirus in human embryonic tissue; this eventually leads to a successful polio vaccine.

invented the transistor. Bardeen became a professor at the University of Illinois in 1951. While there he worked with Cooper and Schrieffer on superconductivity.

In addition to his two Nobel Prizes, John Bardeen has won many scientific awards and honors. These include the Ballentine medal of the Franklin Institute (1952), the Buckley prize (1954), the Scott medal (1955), and the Fritz London Award (1962). Bardeen is also a member of the National Academy of Sciences.

John Franklin Enders

John Franklin Enders (1897-1985) was an American research biologist who made important contributions to vaccines for polio (poliomyelitis), measles, and typhus.

Enders and his co-workers, Frederick Robbins and Thomas Weller, shared the 1954 Nobel Prize for physiology or medicine for their work with the polio virus. In the late 1940's Enders and his research team tried to grow the polio virus in nonnerve tissue. Up to that time, researchers had been able to grow the virus only in the nerve tissue of monkeys. Enders' team found a way to grow the virus in human embryonic tissue. This discovery paved the way for development of a successful polio vaccine by Jonas Salk in 1954. Until the mid-1950's polio had been a widespread, devastating disease that crippled many people in their youth. Later, Enders and his team isolated the three strains of polio virus.

Enders also isolated the measles virus and helped develop a measles vaccine. This vaccine became available in 1963.

John Franklin Enders was born in Connecticut. He received a Masters degree in English Literature at Harvard University in 1922. He later turned to studies of bacteria and received his Ph.D. in this field from Harvard in 1930. For many years, Enders was on the faculty at Harvard. Enders also did consulting work for the U.S. War Department and for the U.S. Army during and after World War II. This work included studies of the mumps virus and Rickettsial diseases. The latter are diseases, such as typhus and Rocky Mountain spotted fever, caused by a particular family of one-celled organisms. In 1946 Enders established a laboratory at Children's Hospital in Boston. Much of

his research on viruses was conducted there. In addition to the 1954 Nobel Prize, Enders won the Presidential Medal of Freedom in 1963.

Rosalind Elsie Franklin

Rosalind Elsie Franklin (1920-1958) was a British scientist who made important contributions to our understanding of complex organic molecules. Franklin used X-ray diffraction techniques to study crystal structures of molecules such as DNA. In X-ray diffraction, X rays are focused on a bit of material containing crystals of the substance to be studied. The atoms in crystals are arranged in planes, with regular spacing between each plane. When an X-ray beam travels through a crystal, the planes of atoms diffract, or spread apart, the rays into a regular pattern. Scientists can then study the diffraction patterns to learn more about the molecular structure of the substance.

In 1951 Franklin began studying DNA crystals at the Biophysical Laboratory of King's College, London. Using X-ray diffraction studies, she discovered a number of important properties of DNA. One of these properties is the helical structure of DNA, that is, its spiral shape. Another is the density of DNA. These discoveries helped James Watson and Francis Crick make an accurate model of the DNA molecule several years later.

Building on her work with DNA, Franklin determined the structure of the tobacco mosaic virus. A virus is a complex molecule that has some characteristics of a living cell.

In other X-ray diffraction research, Franklin analyzed structural changes in heated carbons. This work provided information that proved useful in the coking industry and in atomic technology.

Rosalind Elsie Franklin was born in London in 1920. She studied at Cambridge University, graduating in 1941. After graduation, Franklin worked for the British Coal Utilisation Research Association. In the late 1940's she studied X-ray diffraction techniques with Jacques Méring in Paris. In 1951 Franklin joined the Biophysical Laboratory at King's College, London. From 1953 to 1958 she worked in the Crystallography Laboratory at Birbeck College, London. Rosalind Franklin died in 1958 at the age of 37.

Late Twentieth Century——1950-Today

Jonas Salk announces the development of the first trial polio vaccine.

The Soviet Union launches *Sputnik I,* the first artificial satellite.

| ca. 1952-1953 | 1953 | 1955 | 1957 |

Rosalind Elsie Franklin discovers the helical structure of DNA.

Francis Crick, with **James Watson,** creates a three-dimensional model of the DNA molecule.

Owen Chamberlain and **Emilio Segre** discover the antiproton.

Francis Crick

Francis Crick (1916-   ) is a British biologist who with James Watson made a three-dimensional model of the DNA molecule in 1953. This work won for Crick, Watson, and Maurice Wilkins the 1962 Nobel Prize for Physiology or Medicine. Determining the structure of DNA has proved to be one of the most important discoveries of the twentieth century. The amazing developments in genetics and related fields during the last 30 years would have been impossible without this basic understanding of DNA.

In the late 1940's and early 1950's Crick was doing research at Cambridge University's Medical Research Council Unit of the Cavendish Laboratory. The arrival of American biologist James Watson at the laboratory in 1951 marked the beginning of collaborative effort to map the structure of DNA. Watson predicted that if the three-dimensional molecular structure of DNA could be determined, the substance's role in heredity would become obvious. He convinced Crick that they should start work on this project.

Crick and Watson used the X-ray diffraction studies of DNA carried out by Wilkins, the other eventual recipient of the Nobel Prize, in their work. They developed a model to represent DNA's molecular structure that consisted of two twisted molecular strands connected horizontally by linking strands. Each part of the structure had its own particular set of chemical characteristics. When viewed as a physical model, the structure looked somewhat like a twisted ladder.

Watson's prediction proved accurate. When the researchers studied the DNA model, they were able to show how genes and chromosomes copy their genetic information in dividing cells and how the repeating chemical patterns in the molecular structure carry the genetic code.

Later, Crick was able to demonstrate the connection between coded sections of the DNA structure and the makeup of proteins produced in living cells. Subsequent research in genetics has further confirmed the correctness of Crick and Watson's original work.

Francis Crick was born in Northampton, England. He studied at London and Cambridge Universities. Crick began his career as a physicist and made contributions to the development of radar during World War II. After the war, Crick turned to the field of biology.

Crick authored several books. In *Of Molecules and Men* (1966) he discussed the ongoing revolution in molecular biology and what it would mean to humankind. His controversial book *Life Itself* speculates that life on earth arose from bacteria that came from outside the solar system.

Rachel Carson

Rachel Carson (1907-1964) was an American marine biologist who publicized her scientific concerns in several highly popular books. Carson's most famous work, *Silent Spring*, published in 1962, has probably had a greater impact on the environmental movement than any other book. In *Silent Spring*, Rachel Carson warned the public of the dangers of continual, unrestricted use of pesticides. These human-made chemicals are used to kill crop pests, such as insects. Carson showed how pesticides could pass from farmland into the food of birds and fish and then be passed up the food chain. The book gained a worldwide audience. Since the time of its publication, many countries have passed laws to restrict or ban certain pesticides.

Rachel Carson was born in Pennsylvania. She received a master's degree from Johns Hopkins University in 1932. After doing some further studies at Woods Hole Marine Biological Laboratory, Carson joined the U.S. Bureau of Fisheries, which later became part of the U.S. Fish and Wildlife Service. Carson spent most of her career with this government service.

In addition to *Silent Spring*, Carson published *The Sea Around Us*. This important, popular book describes the biology, chemistry, geography, and history of the oceans and seas. Carson's other writings include *Under the Sea-Wind* (1941) and *The Edge of the Sea* (1955).

Dorothy Crowfoot Hodgkin

Dorothy Crowfoot Hodgkin (1910-   ), a British chemist, won the 1964 Nobel Prize in chemistry for determining the highly complex

---

Theodore H. Maiman builds the first laser.

Rachel Carson publishes *Silent Spring,* awakening America to the problems of pollution.

Radio astronomers discover primordial, background radiation in the universe; this is believed to orginate in the "big bang."

| 1960 | 1961 | 1962 | 1964 | 1965 | 1969 |

Yuri Gagarin, a Russian cosmonaut, becomes the first human to orbit the earth in a spaceship.

Dorothy Crowfoot Hodgkin wins the Nobel Prize for determining the structure of the vitamin B$_{12}$ molecule.

The United States makes the first manned landing on the moon.

structure of the vitamin B$_{12}$ molecule. She has also determined the molecular structure of cholesterol iodide, penicillin, insulin, and other organic compounds. Such studies are of practical importance in medicine. For example, expanded knowledge about the B$_{12}$ molecule has led to better understanding of how the body uses this substance to build red blood cells. This knowledge has, in turn, led to successful treatment of a disease called pernicious anemia.

Hodgkin has used the technique of X-ray diffraction in her analysis of organic compounds. X-ray diffraction is a valuable tool that has aided chemists in understanding the molecular structure of many substances, including DNA. This technique is based on diffraction properties of X rays. When the X rays are focused on a crystalline substance, the regular, repeating arrangement of molecules in the crystals diffracts, or bends, the X rays. The pattern of the X-ray diffraction, which is also regular, can be studied. From these studies, chemists can determine the actual molecular structure of the crystals.

Dorothy Hodgkin was born Dorothy Crowfoot in Cairo, Egypt. Educated in England, she graduated from Oxford University in 1931 and joined its faculty in 1934. She has conducted most of her research at Oxford. Hodgkin is a member of the Royal Society.

Barbara McClintock

Barbara McClintock (1902-   ) is an American geneticist who discovered that genes, which dictate the function of cells and physical traits in plants and animals, move in unpredictable ways. Until McClintock's discovery, it was believed that genes, like pearls on a string, were fixed on the chromosome. In 1983, McClintock was awarded the Nobel Prize in physiology or medicine for this discovery of "mobile genetic elements."

Barbara McClintock began her study of mobile genetic elements in the early 1940's, soon after she joined the Carnegie Institution of Washington, D.C. Working at Cold Spring Harbor, New York, the site of the Carnegie Institution's genetics laboratory, McClintock planted fields of maize for genetic study. She had discovered earlier that Indian corn was an ideal

subject of study because of the unique pigmented patterns of the kernels and leaves.

McClintock first developed the necessary techniques for identifying, visualizing, and characterizing the chromosomes of maize. Eventually, she discovered that while the pattern of pigmentation of maize kernels and leaves were, generally, passed from generation to generation, there were occasional exceptions. This occasional exception, or mutation, triggered McClintock's interest.

McClintock explored the mutation of pigmentation patterns. She concluded, finally, that the genes that determine the color or pattern of a kernel of maize can be switched on and off by a "genetic element"; this genetic element can move from one part of a chromosome to another; and this "mobile genetic element" is controlled or commanded by a third type of element, which she called an "activator." She also concluded that the activator's command of the mobile genetic element, that is, the "jumping" gene, could be triggered by environmental stress, for example, drought. She referred to this state of stress as "genomic shock." "Genomic" derives from "genome," which means the sum of all the chromosomes and their genes within each nucleus of any species. Thus, severe exterior conditions can trigger shock to chromosomes, which in turn triggers immediate change in the genes that control the function of cells and the physical traits passed to the next generation.

The ramifications of this discovery were, and are, enormous. If maize genes were capable of moving about due to some kind of "stress" situation, then the genes of all living things, including the genes of higher life forms, were capable of moving about, triggering change in the next generation of the organism. Although McClintock has refused to speculate on what has not, as yet, been documented, other geneticists see a link between mobile genetic elements and evolutionary change in plants and animals. Also, physiologists see a possible link between mobile genetic elements and the transformation of normal cells into malignant, or cancerous, cells.

In 1951, Barbara McClintock published her discovery. Most of the scientific community were, however, either unwilling or unable to grasp the idea that genes were capable of movement, let alone that genes were capable of rearrangement due to "genomic shock." For the most part, Barbara McClintock's ideas were ignored. The slow acceptance of her dis-

A 1941 photograph of **Barbara McClintock** at work at the Carnegie Institution of Washington genetics laboratory at Cold Spring Harbor, New York

John Bardeen, Leon Cooper, and **John Robert Schrieffer** receive a Nobel Prize in physics for developing the theory of superconductivity.

Scientists use genetically engineered bacteria to produce human insulin.

| 1972 | 1974 | 1978 | ca. 1980 |

Burton Richter and **Samuel C.C. Ting** discover the *psi* particle, a type of elementary particle.

Geneticists produce recombinant DNA in bacteria.

coveries did not, however, seem to bother Miss McClintock. She continued her solitary research. The world did not begin to catch up with Barbara McClintock until the 1960's and 1970's when highly technical research conducted by molecular biologists began to confirm her earlier findings.

Barbara McClintock was born in Hartford, Connecticut. She received her Ph.D. degree from Cornell University in 1927. She stayed at Cornell until 1931, and worked briefly at the California Institute of Technology and the University of Missouri.

McClintock has remained a member of the Carnegie Institution of Washington since 1941. Before being awarded the Nobel Prize, Miss McClintock received the Wolfe Prize in Medicine and the Lasker Award. In 1981 she became the John D. and Catherine T. MacArthur Foundation's first Prize Fellow Laureate.

Stephen William Hawking

Stephen William Hawking (1942-   ) is a British theoretical physicist. Because of his work in the field of gravity, Hawking is considered perhaps the most brilliant theoretical physicist working today.

A 1988 photograph of **Stephen Hawking** in a Cambridge classroom.

Hawking's best-known work is on the nature of black holes, a phenomenon suggested by Einstein's equations describing what might happen should a huge star die, proposing it would crush into its own center with such strong gravitational force that nothing could escape, not even light. Introducing his own theoretical modifications, Hawking posits the existence of mini-black holes. Created by the tremendous force of the big bang, these mini-black holes would not only emit sub-atomic particles and radiation (now called Hawking radiation), but would gradually evaporate over the space of 10^{66} years, only to explode with the energy of millions of hydrogen bombs. At the same time, Hawking is the first to admit that there is as yet no physical evidence that black holes actually exist.

Hawking is one of a number of scientists concerned with theories linking quantum mechanics and gravitation. The premise of these so-called grand unified theories is that it is scientifically possible to prove how the universe came into being.

Hawking was born in Oxford, England. After graduating from Oxford in 1962, he went on to study at Cambridge. In his first year there, he was diagnosed with amyotrophic lateral sclerosis (ALS), otherwise known as Lou Gehrig's disease, an incurable disease of the nervous system. Confined to a wheelchair, he speaks through a computer synthesizer, and his movement is limited to a barely perceptible lifting of one finger and very little facial expression.

Hawking received his Ph.D. degree in 1966 from Cambridge, where he now holds the prestigious post of Lucasian professor of mathematics, a post once occupied by Sir Isaac Newton.

Hawking was among the youngest inductees into the Royal Society, one of the world's most renowned scientific bodies. He has also received the prestigious Albert Einstein Award, has been named Commander of the British Empire by Queen Elizabeth, and has received honorary degrees from Notre Dame, the University of Chicago, Princeton, and New York University. In 1988, he published his book *A Brief History of Time*. He hoped the book would help non-scientists understand theories of nature, from the big bang to black holes.

Chemists begin work on the development of a solar-powered device that produces hydrogen fuel by means of the chemical breakdown of water.

Scientists use genetic engineering to transfer human growth genes into mice, triggering twice-normal growth in the mice.

Stephen William Hawking publishes *A Brief History of Time.*

 ca. 1981   **1983**   **1983**   **1988**

Carlo Rubbia and his research team discover the *W* particle and *Z* particle, two types of subatomic particles.

Barbara McClintock wins the Nobel Prize for physiology or medicine for her discovery that certain genes can change their position on the chromosomes of cells.

Index

Cumulative
Index
to
The World Book Encyclopedia of Science

Each entry in the cumulative index of *The World Book Encyclopedia of Science* is arranged in the following order: Alligator, **6**:74, 79, 141. The darker numbers following the subject entry signifies a single volume of the set. The lighter numbers that follow signify pages within the volume sited. Thus, on pages 74, 79, and 141 of Volume **6**, which is The Animal World, the reader will find references to alligators.

The eight volumes of *The World Book Encyclopedia of Science* are numbered in the following order:

Index

Credits

The following have provided illustrations for this book: Cover photo-Granger Collection; AP/Wide World Photos 88; Bettmann Archive 20, 60, 66, 68, 77, 82; Granger Collection 6, 7, 8, 10, 12, 13, 15, 17, 19, 21, 23, 25, 28, 30, 32, 33, 34, 35, 41, 44, 46, 48, 50, 55, 57, 58, 63, 64, 69, 70, 75, 79; A. Vesalius, *On the Fabric of the Human Body* (1543) 11.